P9-EDT-969

Crocuses and Buffalo Beans

AUGUSTANA UNIVERSITY COLLEGE
LIBRARY

Crocuses
and
Buffalo Beans

by
Flagstaff Creative Writers

Editorial Consultant:
Grant Kennedy

AUGUSTANA UNIVERSITY COLLEGE
LIBRARY

Manitou Press
Killam Alberta Canada

Copyright © 1988 Flagstaff Creative Writers

All rights reserved—no part of this book may be reproduced in any form without permission in writing from Flagstaff Creative Writers.

Photocopying or reproducing mechanically in any other way passages from this book without the written permission of the owner of the copyright is an infringement of the copyright law.

Cover: Courtesy of— The Provincial Museum
                      Edmonton Alberta Canada

Printed by: The Community Press

Dedication

To Eva

Northern Lights

Last night I sat by my window,
With all the lights turned low,
Watching the "Spirit Dancers"
As they hurried to and fro.

I wondered as I watched them,
Pulsing green and rose and blue,
If some of the ancient legends
Might possibly be true.

Much comfort in the thought I find,
That my life-light, set free
Will join with those of friends long gone,
In immortality.

By Eva Cookson

Her spirit dances free.

About
this Book

Flagstaff Creative Writers began in 1973 as a result of a ten week course in *The Basics of Freelance Writing* offered by Margaret Coleman Johnson under the sponsorship of the Literary Arts Branch, Department of Culture, and its first director, John Patrick Gillese.

In 1977, we began publishing "'Riters Ramblings," a weekly column in *The Community Press*, which offered nostalgia, humor, opinion and human interest to the readership through the genres of fiction, nonfiction and poetry. The column was a success for the paper and for us.

Readers frequently gave positive feedback both to the *The Community Press* and to the individual writers. Their encouragement gave the writers the courage to write for other markets as well, and soon members were being published in magazines, newspapers and books across Canada.

Critical approval of the "'Riters Ramblings" project quickly followed. John Patrick Gillese saw the group's scrapbook, read the material, determined its high quality, and arranged for a yearly provincial publishing grant to support it and similar projects undertaken by other writers' groups and local newspapers. When provincial funding ran out, he persuaded the Alberta Weekly Newspaper Association to carry on with the program for a few more years. When that support also disappeared, "'Riters Ramblings" still continued to be published until 1986 when new management at *The Community Press* indicated they were no longer willing to pay the writers even the token fees so long established.

"'Riters Ramblings" ceased to be printed, but continued requests from former readers, and the celebration of our fifteenth anniversary have resulted in this book, a collection of the "The Best of 'Riters Ramblings." We hope you enjoy it.

Flagstaff Creative Writers   November, 1988

Contents

Echoes of Long Ago

Lila J. Davidson

I browse through the history compiled by old friends,
Of places and people I knew
When I was a child. Was it that long ago?
How swiftly, it seems, the years flew.

As I read the stories and as I look back
Recalling my youth once again
It seems the book has left something out
The love, the laughter, the pain.

The past is all tidy and neatly set out
Like the view of a farm from the plane
It looks so precise for from that far away
You can't see the junk in the lane.

In the history book all the scandals are gone
That once had all in a bind.
The grumpy old couple who threw pots and pans
Seem the same as the ones who were kind.

This thought is a solace when troubles arise
And life seems so dull and grey,
Let us remember that time will erase
The pain that we feel today.

In the Midst of Yesterday

Sharleen M. Chevraux

Today I walked with shaggy kings of the past, with buffalo which thundered and fought, played and died a hundred years ago.

The skies were overcast. Small showers had dampened the earth. The fields were beginning to ripen. We were close to harvest.

I found a path through poplar trees and prairie grass sprinkled with golden, white, purple and blue flowers, raspberry bushes and silver willow. The ripening spears were waist high and sticky wet. The trail was almost hidden.

Branches overhead spattered rain droplets until I entered a small clearing and found a small dip in the gentle hollows of the land where shaggy beasts once rolled and pawed and kicked dust over huge, humped bodies.

For a moment I could see them, their massive heads lowered as powerful hooves pummeled the ground to raise thick clouds of dust. They hunched into the wallow and rolled with heavy ecstasy. I could hear their snorts of satisfaction, feel their content as they lurched to their feet and moved to join others of their kind grazing quietly.

Kings of the plains, they had few living enemies, only the grizzly and man.

Man.

An Indian crouched beneath the skin of a buffalo calf, imitating its movements. Another hunter wore wolf's skin and pretended to attack the calf. A bull stopped wallowing to watch. Others of the herd looked up curiously and began to move slowly to the defense of the young.

Swiftly a dozen hunters rose from the grass, shooting arrows at the moving beasts. Several fell. The rest, led by the bull, turned abruptly and thundered away.

They faded and there was only the buffalo grass and a curious deer peering through its spears. A deer that lifted its head, sniffed the scents of summer and man, then bounded gracefully into the trees.

I turned for home. The sun had appeared out of a suddenly blue sky and the path was dappled with light and shade. Dewy diamonds sparkled in the grass and leaves. The path was quiet, peaceful. A place of the past.

The Chatauqua's Coming!

Doris M. Saunders

"The Chatauqua lady is here."

Word passed from one excited student to another. The Chatauqua lady had come to organize a parade of school children. She was as always charming. She taught us songs and Chatauqua cheers.

The day of the parade arrived. We rode ponies and marched down Main Street, singing, cheering and beating tin pie plates while all the shoppers stopped to watch. The oldest school pony led the parade. After the parade, the lady threw peanuts and we scrambled for them.

It was thrilling! Anticipation grew as we learned of the wonders to come. Advertising was studied to see which afternoon or evening we would attend. Times were hard. Our family decided we could buy one adult and one children's ticket. We'd have to take turns.

The Chatauqua programs included lantern slides, lectures, plays, magicians, puppetry, classical and jazz concerts as well as a variety of other entertainment. How would a Swiss yodeller sound? What would Vilhjalmer Stefansson, who had explored the Arctic, tell us? How hard it was to choose! We spent the intervening days savouring the delights of the various programs to come.

We agonized with Stefansson as he endured hardships of cold and darkness in the Arctic. Our spirits soared with the music of Jasha Galprin's violin and we clung to each word of the soprano who sang "One Fine Day" from Madame Butterfly.

On the last night we saw the musical play "Smiling Through." The stage was set with a garden of roses by a little cottage. The lighting so inspired our romantic hearts that we hung on every word till finally the heroine, old and frail, quietly died. At once, her spirit, again young and beautiful, rose from behind the flowers to be joined by her lost love. With arms entwined and smiles on their lips they floated away. The music throbbed. It was so sad, so sad! We cried and thought we had never had such an evening.

We Walked in Beauty

Violet M. Copeland

"Beauty is but skin deep," my grandmother used to say when we girls hung our curling irons upside down over the lamp flame to coax our straight locks into ringlets. For the top of our heads we heated the "double marcel" iron to make waves like railroad tracks in our tresses. Though we arose before dawn for the five-mile ride to school, not one of the 'big girls' would have faced that trip without the comforting knowledge that her hair was properly curled. Better late than straight!

Not every girl chose the risk of the hot curling iron. Some of us wound our hair with strips of rags, emerging curled in the morning. For short hair, the process was a roll-up with ends tied in a tight bow. To curl long hair, teeth and one hand held the strip taut and the other hand wound the hair around it. Then the rag had to be wound around the roll of hair until the ringlet was reached and the knot secured. The whole thing looked like a crown of stiff sausages. It mattered little which method was used. The unhappy victim tossed and turned till morning. Only the promise of lovely corkscrew curls enabled the girls to endure the nightly tribulations.

Nevertheless, we persevered in our self-torture. Presently aluminum and rubber curlers arrived to assist in the nightly ordeal. They were no softer to sleep on. One rubber curler invariably escaped from its slots leaving forty-seven curls and one straight clump, usually right in front. Aluminum curlers fell apart, stabbing the oppressed user.

Finally came permanents. These translated into one afternoon of head-aches with hot, humid curlers tearing at the hair roots. A few dollars would ensure six months or more of glamour. We walked in beauty, true, but how we suffered to achieve it!

The Legacy

Rose Marie Thompson

The spine of the Titanic snaps. It slips, slides, tumbles and sinks, coming to rest in the gold carpet.

I have forgotten. The stop on the underside of "my memory drawer" is broken. Memories clutter the room.

I fall to my knees and gather my treasures. Each one evokes a feeling or conjures up a picture.

I sort letters, report cards, diplomas, post cards and newspaper clippings. "Young Alberta Woman Critically Injured in Tragic Accident." The memory of our daughter stabs my heart. A plastic bag of sand mixed with broken sea shells. "From Glenn, August 1980—Long Beach Sand." Ocean smells fill my nostrils. Seagulls cry. A treasure from our elder son. Bits of blue egg shell are crushed beneath the edge of the drawer, all that remains of a ring box lovingly made by younger son long ago.

A scruffy black Teddy bear with white spots has escaped the carnage. I wind the key embedded in his back and press him to my face. He smells of old saw dust. The tinny sound emanating from his innards brings not a flicker of recognition. Every second note is missing. Plinkety, plunkety sounds break the stillness. A gift from my lover, now my husband. I place Teddy in the drawer alongside a box of letters. He stares balefully at me with his one good eye.

Yellowed pages of the Titanic have fluttered about the room. Gradually I collect them. A small brown box has sprung open and a pipe has fallen out. As I kneel to retrieve these objects, I rest my hand in the carpet and discover the last of my treasures. A clay marble.

A book, a pipe and a marble. My legacy from my Father.

My mind swirls backwards some twenty-five years. My Father is dead. Mother asks if there is anything of his I would like to have. My reply— "His books, his pipe and his clay marbles."

I roll the greyish-brown marble about in my hand. Once there were five. Now, there is just this one.

I am a tiny girl watching my Father reach to the top of the cupboard. From behind the green and white checkered gingham curtain he extracts a wooden cigar box—HIS memory box. From it he takes old coins, medals, ribbons and five clay marbles. He tells me they were his when he was a boy. They were handmade of clay long before marbles were made of glass. They are very old. With me perched on his lap, he sorts through his memories, returns them to the box and replaces it. He kisses me goodnight and by the light of a coal-oil lamp, I climb the steps to bed.

Now, I place the marble in the little brown box and pick up the pipe. "Genuine Imported Briar" it reads on one side. "Old Country" it says on the other. The red bowl is encrusted with the black tars of Old Virginia Pipe Tobacco. The black stem bears his teeth marks. I raise it to my nose and inhale its fragrance.

It's forty years ago and I see Father filling his tobacco pouch from the red tin of Old Virginia. He reams out the bowl of his pipe with his jack-knife and knocks the dottle into the palm of his hand. He fills the pipe with tobacco, tamps it down, strikes a wooden Eddy's match on the seat of his G.W.G. overalls and lights his pipe. He puffs and a sweet cloud of smoke envelops his head. He settles back in his old, wooden rocker and opens a book.

Father disappears as if in a puff of his own tobacco smoke.

Crawling across the carpet on my knees in the ever increasing gloom of late afternoon, I gather the yellowed pages of the book. "The Sinking of the Titanic and Great Sea Disasters—Thrilling Stories of Survivors with Photographs and Sketches" reads the cover which also carries a scarred photo of the tragic ocean liner. The lettering is black and red across a linen cover that might once have been beige but is now dotted with seventy year-old fly specks. The spine is broken, old glue clinging to cheesecloth. In faded red ink on the fly of the book my Father's strong hand had written Maurice A. Stumpf—1912—Hunterville, Alberta.

As I replace pages, a bear of a man in a white uniform stares at me. "Captain E.J. Smith of the ill-fated giant of the sea; a brave and seasoned commander who was carried to his death with his last and greatest ship." Gently, I replace page 179 which contains a partial list of the "Roll of the Dead—First Cabin (continued) beginning with "Beattie, T" and ending with "Ornout, Alfred T." I study the picture of the "Main Stairway on Titanic—Top E Deck" and am reminded of the underwater exploration team which last year photographed this very page from history in the cold waters of the Atlantic.

Once again, the vision of my Father in his rocking chair comes to mind. I see through the smokey haze that his weathered hands turn the pages of this very book.

Gently, I return the "Titanic" to its place alongside my other treasures. The last thing I see as the drawer closes is Teddy's one good eye, staring out of the darkness from where he rests beside the Titanic.

The ZYX Game

Doris M. Saunders

"Don't cry!" I begged my young brother. "The freezing air in your lungs will give you pneumonia again." Our parents had warned that crying could only make us colder.

We were riding double on our old school pony, Duke, who couldn't run fast enough through the deep snow to keep us from nearly freezing in the 20 below zero weather.

Duke waded and puffed and blew steam till it froze and hung down in an icicle from his nose.

Our breath, too, froze on our woollen scarves wound about our necks and heads till only our eyes peeped out. We were bundled in winter clothes, toques, long coats, and large leather mitts lined with a couple of pair of woollen mitts. But still my hands holding the reins were cold and I often slipped my thumbs under my fingers to warm them.

I didn't wear slacks—girls didn't. I wore bloomers, navy blue serge pleated bloomers, into which my dress was stuffed. No matter how nice it looked when I left home, it came out of those bloomers wrinkled-looking. My long coat sort of doubled up under my seat and wouldn't come around my thighs so they got icy cold next to the saddle. On my legs I wore long underwear and heavy ribbed stockings. My feet were encased in several pairs of woollen socks rolled over the top of a pair of beaded moccasins. My feet in the stirrups felt like lumps of ice and I let them hang loose and kicked the horse's sides to make the feeling come back and urge him to hurry.

But eventually it was so cold it was hard not to cry and my little brother's complaints were getting louder. "I'm freezing to death," he cried.

Let's learn the alphabet backwards. Perhaps if we don't think about the cold, it won't be so bad. Let's see, xyz...zyx. What goes next?"

"I don't know, I'm too cold," he wailed. I persisted.

"Zyx...uv."

My brother sniffed loudly. "Ya dummy, it's rstuvwxyz," as he entered into the game.

"Zyxwv...u...tsr."

"Now let's see if we can say it. Zyx...w...v...u..."

"Tsr," he added.

"Now what letter?...Lmnopqr."

"Qpo..." and so it continued by trial and error as the horse loped where he could or plunged through drifts.

"There we've said it all! And thank goodness we've reached the livery stable."

Seeing how cold we were, the kindly livery-stable attendant offered to look after our horse while we ran to school. Our feet felt like blocks of ice and hurt as we tried to hurry, and the increasing frost on our scarves made our noses colder.

At last we were in the school and the tears spilled over as we went to our classrooms. My girl friends helped me unpin the scarf and undo my other clothes. As I fumbled with the buttons I wished the boys wouldn't watch me take off those hated bloomers. I turned my back on them, smoothing my rumpled dress, wiped my reddened eyes and blew my watery nose. I rubbed my hands through my hair to warm them a little as school was about to begin.

Later in the day when my feet were really too warm, the chilblains began to hurt and itch. I tried to scratch but it's not easy to scratch a foot through moccasins and several pairs of socks. The more I tried to scratch, the more my feet itched. I was almost frantic and wished my feet would get cold again to stop the itching. Maybe if I could get my mind off them...Perhaps I should play the game again.

"Zyx..."

Menacing Wall of Sand

Doris Likness

I often wonder if teaching today is the adventure it was in my youth. Years ago, a young teacher usually had to prove competence by acquiring experience in rural schools. Most schools had but one room and outdoor plumbing. In April, 1926, I answered an advertisement in *The Vancouver Province*, "Teachers Needed for Alberta Schools." I, a diminutive miss of 19 years, was soon on my way to big adventure.

"You have reached the end of the world," the train conductor said as we rattled east from Coronation.

It wasn't long before I found myself a member of a delightful family, five of the six children to be my pupils. The house was painted bright green, a cheery oasis amid the brown fields. Mrs. P. was proud of her bathroom, probably the only one in the community. No matter that the water had to be heated on the kitchen stove in a large copper boiler.

The school, in its setting of endless grass, was only a pleasant walk away. There was a picnic spot, too, in the nearby mud buttes which resembled miniature "badlands." They were great to explore, a curious phenomenon in the vast prairie landscape.

School had been dismissed one day and I was busy marking papers. "Teacher!" Fifteen-year-old Harry had returned.

"Yes?"

"There's a sandstorm coming and I think it's going to be real bad," he said.

"Thanks, Harry. I'll leave pretty soon," I assured him.

It was only about five minutes later I began to notice an ominous darkness enveloping the room. I rushed to the west window and what I saw put wings to my feet. I put on my small straw hat, grabbed my lunch pail and ran down the road. Would that great wall of dust, ugly, black and menacing, be upon me before I could reach safety? It was advancing at a tremendous rate, long streamers writhing and swirling higher and higher above the horizon. With frantic haste, I ran along the plowed field, panting and gasping for fear.

All at once I was enshrouded in that vast terrifying sheet of dirt. Was that a telephone pole in front of me? I put my arms about it and clung to it desperately. The pole shivered and shook and so did I. My eyes, ears, nose and mouth were soon choked with dirt.

Out of the murky darkness I heard a welcome voice: "You poor little thing! Were you frightened?" Big, kind Mr. P. had come to my rescue. He put his arms about me to shield me from the flying debris.

Soon it was clear enough for us to battle our way toward the house. There Mrs. P. had warm water ready for a bath which soothed and cleansed my battered body. A hot cup of tea eased my smarting throat.

"The Dirty Thirties"

Doris M. Saunders

A black cloud of dust rolled high in the western sky as the wind blew fiercely. Our tall spruce tree flung its head wildly, scattering cones across the lawn. "Oh no, not here too," I thought. I grew up on the treeless prairie and there had been nothing to break the ferocity of the wind. This sky and the wind were similar to those in "The Dirty Thirties." And they were dirty years.

The first storms we experienced in the thirties had my father hurrying us all down cellar against the west wall for safety in case the house blew away. The sky darkened till we had to put the lights on; we were scared. The windows rattled as the house groaned and creaked on its foundation.

Russian thistles rolled and bounced across the prairie until they came to rest against a fence high enough to catch them. Some fences almost disappeared in the piles of top soil blown from miles away.

Dust piled up on sills and floors, sneaking in every possible crack so that it was over everything. After the storm had blown itself out, we swept as much as we could into the dust pan, but the rest had to be washed up. There was no other way.

It nearly always happened that dust storms struck on Friday or Saturday night when the house had been cleaned from top to bottom, ready for Sunday. It was discouraging to have to begin again.

I remember one dust storm that caught me on my way to school. The sky looked awesome. I was frightened. I turned the horse to flee towards home but that idea was soon abandoned as I realized I'd never make it. In desperation I climbed from the horse and lay face down in the ditch. The horse turned his back to the storm and lowered his head, snorting the dust from his nostrils. I hung on to the tufts of grass and pressed my body close to the earth. The wind didn't seem so bad down there and my pounding heart slowed. When the worst of the storm had blown over, I mounted my horse and with head down, braved the wind. Dust clogged my nose and grated on my teeth. My eyes looked like holes in a black face when I arrived.

Farmers dreaded winds that made soil drift like snow, cutting off tender young grain and blackening the greening fields. Many a crop had to be replanted and farmers couldn't afford that.

Those days are gone and we now live in the parkland, but when I see the brushing about potholes and roadsides, I fear for the land. I remember that menacing black dust cloud.

Flour Sack Magic

Doris M. Saunders

A flour sack is a little girl's dress, a tablecloth, a tea towel, pot holders, some curtains, a patch work bedspread, a dresser scarf or a pair of bloomers.

In my younger days you never threw a flour sack away. It was carefully opened when empty, either by unpicking each stitch or by carefully choosing the right thread and pulling to unravel the stitching. It was washed, boiled, and bleached to remove the colored paint. You never knew what article it would end up being.

With some embroidery and a bit of lace it became a pillow case. Hem it and you had a giant size tea towel or cut it in half for two smaller ones.

There were tea towels with designs for every day of the week embroidered on them—a gift fit for a new bride.

Aprons with rick rack trim or bias binding were nice for home use or a bazaar. A bit of print material could make a lot of difference when added to plain unbleached flour bags if you had done a really good job of eliminating the colored printing.

Kitchen curtains with print applique lifted your spirits on dull days. If you were ambitious, you could embroider patches and sew them together to make colorful patchwork quilts.

When flour companies realized what women were doing with flour sacks, they decided to make them more attractive to boost sales. They used floral prints and pink and blue gingham bags. A paper sticker which could easily be removed told the name of the product.

These pink and blue checked bags could easily end up as a little girl's dress made with frills, lace or contrasting bias tape.

The possibilities were endless. One large woman made herself a pair of voluminous bloomers. Perhaps she didn't know how to remove the bright printing, or perhaps she thought by numerous washings it would fade. Anyway, the printing wouldn't matter because she didn't expect to be showing her bloomers, but a gale one day whipped her dress up enough for all the world to see "Robin Hood Flour" emblazoned across her behind.

What's a flour sack?

Stooks and the New Driver

Rose Marie Thompson

V-shaped formations of geese honked their way south. Smells of harvest were in the air. Stalks of golden wheat, heads heavy, waved gently under clear skies. In a few weeks it would be that magical season—threshing time; but now was the time to cut and stook the grain. It was a Wednesday, September, 1948.

For days Dad and Uncle labored daily in the fields, the little green John Deere tractor pulling the McCormick binder endlessly around fields of ripened grain. Chuck—chucka—clack—bang, the old binder cut, tied and spit the bundles into the catcher. Pull the trip, dump them in rows, stook them. That's where we children came in.

Harvest time in the 1940's meant everyone pitched in. We children were expected to be home promptly after school, to change clothes quickly, and to head to the fields to help. Other farm chores and homework came later.

Our feet passed quickly through yellow stubble, stirring up grasshoppers which leaped before us as we headed for the south-east quarter. To the first row of bundles we went and in shimmering heat, built the stooks.

Bindering did not stop for meals but continued until moist evening air toughened the grain and failing light called a halt for the day. When the supper hour approached, Dad and Uncle halted near where my brother and I worked so two of us might go for supper.

Dad climbed stiffly from the tractor as he and I would go first. We trudged to the edge of the field where the dusty, blue 1946 Chevy stood in the late afternoon heat. From the shady side of the car, Dad retrieved a two-quart sealer, removed the ever-present pipe from his mouth and drank thirstily of the warm water. With work-roughened hand, he wiped away the water which trickled down the sides of his chin, wetting his three-day growth of stubble. Dad shaved on Saturdays for town and Sundays for church.

He allowed the water to quench his thirst, while with eyes shaded with dampened hand, he stared into the distance. He gazed westwards to the hazy peaks of the Rocky Mountains, crests already tipped with snow. Slowly his gaze drifted southward, following the line of the mountains until suddenly he exclaimed: "Look, you can see Carstairs. It's a mirage."

My eyes followed his pointing finger. Wavering in the autumn heat was the town of Carstairs, many miles distant. No way from our farm east of Olds could one see Carstairs on most days, but every once in a while, heat and light joined forces to produce this optical phenonomen. Together we marvelled at this strange sight which never seemed to lose its fascination.

Time was passing. Dad started towards the driver's side of the Chev. Part way around he stopped, looked at me and asked: "How would you like to drive the car home? I'll give you your first driving lesson."

My twelve year old heart leaped. I drive the car? Well, I guess! Smiling delightedly, I slipped behind the wheel.

Dad wearily got in the passenger side. "Go ahead. You know how to start it," he said. "Now you'll have to get turned around here in the field to get through the gate back there."

I turned the key in the ignition. The engine surged to life. I shifted into first. With steering wheel cranked as far to the right as it would go, I eased my foot from the clutch and stepped on the gas. Lurch—lurch—and the car leaped into action. We began circling the field as if that car was possessed. Around and around we went. Stooks were flying, wheat bundles crashing on hood, on windshield and over the top.

"Step on the brake." Dad had really come to life.

My response was to tromp down hard on the accelerator. Thump, thump thump —there went another 50 stooks as we swept outwards in ever-widening circles. At this rate we might not need the threshing crew. I seemed to be doing their job. Wheat and chaff filled the air.

We got paid a penny a stook plus a nickel a round for running the binder or tractor. If I didn't get that blasted car stopped, I might end up paying for the privilege of working come the end of harvest.

My hands were frozen to the wheel; my right foot to the gas pedal. In desperation, Dad turned the key in the ignition, and after another ten stooks were knocked over, we rolled to a stop.

Dad could cuss when the situation demanded and he did a little then. Although weary, he sprang from the passenger side and hot-footed it around the back of the car. No way was he going to walk in front of the car with me still at the wheel and the car in gear. As he tore around the rear, a loose seam on his G.W.G.'s caught on the edge of the bumper. By this time, he had built up such momentum that his overalls were ripped from waist to ankle.

The clear autumn air turned a different shade of blue.

For several minutes he stood silently at the back of the car, puffing his pipe and surveying the damage. I sat glued to the seat, keeping a low profile. Slowly, he walked to where I waited. His tanned face broke into a grin. "Better move over, little girl, and let me drive. You've done enough damage for one day."

With Dad at the wheel, the dusty Chevy turned neatly in the field and headed home for supper.

My Roundup

Betty Walsh

"I'll go and get the horses," I volunteered, anxious to prove my willingness to learn about farm life and work.

My husband looked doubtful. He was remembering the time I had tried to entice Ace and Nickle into the barn with a bucket of oats. They had followed eagerly but were so big with their hot breath ruffling my hair and large hoofs nearly treading on my heels that I had dropped the bucket and ran.

"I know them better now," I insisted. "I'd like to get them."

He still looked doubtful but agreed to stay at the house with the children and handed me the halter shanks.

It was a beautiful morning in late May, I took a shortcut through an over-grown garden patch. I knew I should have taken the lane when I tripped over some concealed barb wire, cutting my leg and scraping my knees. After repairing the damage as best I could and checking to see how badly my skirt was torn, I was on my way again.

It took me ten minutes to get the pasture gate open. Too long! I really should have had sense enough to turn back and let Jim get the horses but when I make up my mind I don't willingly change it. It's called stubborness.

Once inside, I propped that gate shut as I wasn't risking another fight to open it when I was leading those horses. Not seeing them, I called and gave a whistle as I'd heard Jim do, and stood waiting for some sign of Ace and Nickle. No results. I started off to the bush, stopping to call and whistle every few minutes. I walked and called, called and walked.

It was getting hot when I saw the horses standing quietly by the fence in the farthest corner of the field. They stood there looking at me as I walked cautiously up to them. I snapped the rope onto Nickle's bridle and turned to do the same to Ace.

Big black Ace had a different idea. He shied and charged away. Nickle thought he'd follow and tried to pull the rope from my hand. I hung on tightly and started after Ace. He had only gone a little way along the fence line where he stood watching me. I advanced carefully, clutching Nickle's rope tightly. Twice he wheeled around and raced away. The third time he left it too late and I managed to grab his halter and hang on.

I led them both to the fence where I wrapped Nickle's rope around a fence post. Thank goodness he stood quietly while I snapped the rope onto Ace's halter. Now I'd got them both, I started towards the gate.

They followed meekly for awhile. Then Ace jerked his head up and brought his chin down hard on my shoulder. The shock made me release my grip on his rope and he was away again. Red-faced and very annoyed, I led Nickle to the gate and tied him to a fence post.

I hurried back to catch Ace again. I whistled and called. He'd stay just so far away, then take off when I was near enough to make a grab for him. He finally stopped too long at a special patch of grass and I grabbed that rope and hung on. Back to Nickle. Red-faced, perspiring, exhausted, with a sore shoulder and knees, I led those two big brutes up the lane to the yard.

Jim was just coming out of the house carrying the baby with son beside him. "I was coming to look for you. You've been gone two hours. Did you have much trouble catching them?" he asked.

"Of course not," I replied. "I just called and they came. I was gone so long and I look like this because I took them for a run so they'd not be so skittish when you hitched them to the buggy!"

I knew he didn't believe me!

Berry Time

Blanche McGowan

Berries—big, juicy, berries. All kinds bring back memories of when berries were our main source of fruit.

As the school term was ending and the strawberries were beginning, we used to pick them in the ditches as we went home from writing a final exam. Most of the summer was spent picking berries of one kind or another. We would take our lunch and pick wild strawberries until our containers were full. Mother canned; we picked, my sisters and I.

Next came the saskatoons. My aunt would take the truck, and all the neighbors. The kids piled in the back with the cream cans and pails. This was our summer picnic. Every family took something for lunch, even homemade ice cream.

There were bets on who would pick the most berries or talk the most. I think I qualified for both.

Once when we were going back on the trail to the main road, the trees were close. One of the boys grabbed a tree and was almost swung out of the truck. It jerked his arm and shoulder, a lesson to all of us, but it didn't stop us from singing, laughing and talking.

Another time, I found a patch of big juicy saskatoons on short bushes. Everything was fine until a swarm of bees attacked me. I got a good number of bites on my eyelids and cheeks before I got out of there. I screamed but no one came at first. They thought I was fooling around. Someone poured water on the ground and made a mud pack to put on my face. That day was ruined.

Next came the raspberries. We picked all day and mother canned dozens of jars of fruit, or made jams or jellies. Our place had so many berries, especially in a tree patch that a fire had gone through. People came from town to pick on the roadsides, and in our bushes. Some had to be asked not to make tracks through the crops from bush to bush. People pulled up plants, sat in the shade to pick the berries off and left piles of canes.

We used to carve our initials in a tree the day we picked berries . I often wonder if that tree is still there.

I remember when my sister told me to put my hand in a hole in a tree. There was a woodpecker setting there and she almost took my finger off.

We always took the dog with us to warn us if there was unwanted company like a porcupine or skunk in the underbrush. If Ol' Sport barked, we tore out of there like we'd been shot at.

Choke-cherries, pin cherries and goose berries were also plentiful on the road sides. There aren't many today because of sprays and road-side brushing.

That Time of Year

Doris Likness

It's that time of year!

Temperatures soar; the covering mantle of snow disappears; yards look grubby. Within each house dusty corners are exposed. Determined women produce mops, detergents, cleaning fluids and vacuums. For a week, perhaps even two, the household is in chaos.

Today's mad rush at the residues of winter are a far cry from those of fifty years ago. The carpet sweeper did the best it could, but it was no match for the modern vacuum cleaner.

Skipping home from school one long ago noon, I entered our yard from the back alley and I knew something was up. Carpets hung on our clotheslines, too heavy to swing in the breeze. Dodging under them, I hurried up the steps into our kitchen. Walter and Audrey were there before me, sensing as I did that something was amiss. No good smell of cooking on our big black stove! No table set for lunch! Mama came bustling in, aproned and smudged, saying cheerfully, "Just sandwiches today, children. Katie and I are house-cleaning."

I peeked through the swinging door into our dining room. Such a mess! A clutter of chairs, and a table covered with geraniums, while nude windows gazed forlornly across the fence to the house next door. I sniffed. The smell of paint, varnish and cleaning fluid made me crinkle my nose. The living room beyond the double doors, divested of all removable furniture, looked huge in its emptiness. The big piano and our sofa were shoved askew. Walls were bereft of pictures. The floor looked sad in its nakedness. Katie, perched on a step-ladder, had no time for small talk.

"Come," Mother ordered, "and have your sandwiches. You can eat your apples on the way to school. After school, come right home. I have some jobs for you."

I wondered what she had planned for us.

After school Mama gave Walter, Audrey and me each a stick or broom in order to attack the carpets. We beat until the dust came flying out. Walter was best. Audrey and I had limited success.

Maudie called over the fence, "Aren't you going to play hop-scotch with us?" We hop-scotched at school, we hop-scotched at home. Sometimes we skipped rope or played 'odd or even' with marbles for a change.

"I can't," I cried. "I have to help Mama house clean." I banged the stiff carpet as spirals of dust blew about my head. Mama came to examine our success in beating her precious old things. Her report to Katie wasn't very flattering. Our strong, sturdy Katie came striding out, a gleam in her eye. She grabbed my broom. Bang! Bang! Dust flew in earnest. I ran, glad to escape, hop-scotch on my mind. Only Walter stuck to the miserable task.

Before I could get away, Mother called. Reluctantly, I turned back. She beckoned me inside. Pointing to a small box filled with fine china ornaments, she said, "Your next job is to wash these, Doris. You must be very careful with them."

The upheaval in our home seemed to last forever. Every room, every picture, every drawer, had to be gone over or gone through. At last, shining windows, fresh curtains, dust-free carpets, newly painted or papered walls attested to the world that our house was ready for spring. I could breathe again, skip rope or hop-scotch to my heart's delight. Only now it was softball time, Anti-I-Over or Run Sheep Run. How glad I was house cleaning time was over.

Money Didn't Grow on Our Bushes

Doris M. Saunders

The crop was harvested, the bins were full and some wagon loads had been hauled to the elevator, but times were hard. Wheat was selling for twenty-five cents a bushel.

The Eaton's and Simpson's catalogues arrived and we children spent many exciting hours pouring over their contents.

At last Mother sat down to make out the order for household goods and winter clothes.

We each told her what we'd like. She wrote the order for what she thought was needed. It was a big order which covered three pages of forms. This was the only way we had of shopping as no store in the area carried the things we needed and we didn't often go to a larger centre.

There was long underwear for all the family except Mother. Heavy winter socks and stockings, winter mitts. Perhaps a new coat if the old one was too small or too worn to be handed down to the next in line. I, being the only girl, got my cousin's cast off clothes. Occasionally, I would have a new dress which was saved "for good."

Other clothes were made by Mother from material chosen from the colorful pages of fabrics illustrated in the catalogues. I was lucky if I had a skirt and a couple of sweaters to wear to school.

At last the order was finished and totaled. Then it had to have my father's approval. He took one look and roared, "I can't afford to buy all these things. We have to have money for groceries."

He went over that order item by item.

"What's this? Woollen mitts? You don't need those."

"But the boys need new ones. The old ones are worn out," protested Mother.

"Then I'll make some out of old socks." The pencil stroked them out.

"What's this dress?"

"It's for Doris. She needs a new one for winter."

"Find a cheaper one!" The pencil moved again.

So it went until there were more items blacked out than there were left. I fled to my room to cry.

Mother was almost in tears too as she took out a new order form. She was ashamed to send her order marked up as it was so she began once more, muttering to herself, "I've just got to have things for the children." She put a few items back in again.

At last it was finished and we watched, holding our breaths while father looked it over.

"Well, that's better. You know money doesn't grow on the bushes around here."

Sliver Pants

Rose Marie Thompson

The year was 1940. I was a child of the prairies and few things were forbidden in our home but the number one commandment seemed to be, "Thou shalt not climb on the roofs of buildings."

When you are four, a sloped roof looks exactly like a giant slide. That such a roof is not made of the same material as a playground slide or that cedar shingles present problems not associated with a shiny piece of metal escaped my attention.

All the roofs looked inviting. However, when you are three feet tall, a barn roof looks awesome. The roof of the pig stable looked good, but if I fell, I'd fall in the piggy-poo. The ride down the outhouse would be much too short. The house was definitely out because they'd hear me on the roof, just like the reindeer in the poem "The Night Before Christmas" which I had recited at the Christmas concert.

That left only one choice—the chicken coop. It was perfect. It wasn't too big. It had a good sized roof. Best of all, a barbed-wire fence ran along the lower slope.

I climbed up three strands of wire, stood on the top of the fence post and hoisted myself up. I clambered on the top, sat down and began my descent. If everything had gone according to plan, I would have swooshed down the roof, shot off the edge, sailed through the air and landed on the ground, an instant statistic; but thermal snuggies do not slide down a splintery, cedar shingle roof. What happens is that the dry, grey slivers slide through the holes in the pink, thermal snuggies and embed themselves in the soft, white underside of a four year old girl.

I hadn't gone more than six feet when I found myself stuck to the roof like a fly to flypaper. My backside felt like my dog Peter's nose must have felt the day he decided to investigate the porcupine.

I had little thought of the consequences of having broken commandment number one. I wanted someone to find me, unstick me from that roof, and make the pain go away. My wailing equalled the ruckus created by twenty-four pot lids being banged at a shivaree.

Dad came flying out of the barn. "What are you doing up there?" he shouted.

"I'm stuck."

Dad extracted me from my predicament and lowered me to the outstretched arms of Mother.

For weeks I soaked in warm epsom salts sitz baths and underwent daily extraction processes with tweezers as those slivers festered their way out of my bottom.

To me, there was a direct connection between the tiny openings in the fabric of those snuggies and my pain. They alone were the cause of my predicament. I became convinced that if I wore those snuggies again, slivers would find their way through those little openings. It never occurred to me that if I didn't attempt to slide down a shingled roof, the same fate would not befall me.

Unlike old Peter, who never seemed to learn not to stick his nose in a porcupine, I learned never to wear thermal snuggies under any circumstance.

For me, there never was a spring or fall in the underwear seasons. I went straight from the white, cotton briefs of summer to the purple-dashed, fleece-lined bloomers of winter with nary a snuggie in between—or another sliver.

Saturday Pennies

Betty Walsh

We never touched them until we'd finished eating although they were there by our plates every Saturday. But once we'd eaten dinner and recited our "Thank God for our good dinner. Amen. Please-may-I-get-down," we grabbed those precious pennies as we slid from our chairs.

Those pennies felt so good in our hands—not the little pennies of today but the big pennies that we had in England in the nineteen twenties. The two Saturday pennies were special. Whether they were thin and worn or fat and shiny, they were meant for only one thing—to spend right away on sweets.

As soon as mother had checked hands and faces, we were off racing up the road to find ourselves in no time at all in front of the sweet shop. We didn't go in right away. First the three of us (later the four) would stand gazing in the window while weighing in our minds the virtues of everything. We could get a lot more raspberry drops than we could peppermint fudge. But the fudge was so good, mellow on our tongues like a bar of chocolate. Again, we could get a lot of aniseed balls and they lasted a long time. We gazed and talked while we pondered. Then the thrill of opening the door with its important sounding bell which summoned one of the two plump sisters who kept the shop.

Ordering might take a while as it was almost unheard of to spend both pennies on one thing. Why buy all of one kind when we could buy at least two or three or four kinds if we wanted to go into half pennies. A ha'penny worth of coconut ice (pink and white fudge), a ha'penny worth of raspberry drops and a penny bar of Nestle's milk chocolate made a good variety. How about a penny worth of fudge (peppermint, vanilla or chocolate), a ha'penny worth of butterscotch and a ha'penny of aniseed balls? For a real mixture, a ha'penny each of pear drops, dolly mixture, chocolate drops and toffee sounded good. There were also fruit drops, barley sugar, all sorts of chocolate bars, nougat, liquorice. We were in that little shop a long time.

We surrendered our precious pennies and watched as each selection was weighed in the shiny brass scales and put in a little paper bag. No mixing. Each selection separate so that at times we were given four bags to clutch in our hands. Polite goodbyes said, we burst from the shop and streaked for home.

Once home, there was the important business of "swapping."

"I'll give you a piece of fudge for two raspberry drops."

"No, but you can have two aniseed balls for a piece of coconut ice."

"No, I don't want aniseed balls. I want raspberry drops."

We each had our own place for our sweets and no one ever ate anyone else's. We made them last several days. I often think of those days when I'm trying to decide between a Mars Bar and a Caramilk, or watch a youngster weighing the merits of gum or chips. My choice seems unimportant now but I wonder if they experience the excitement of those special afternoons when I spent my Saturday pennies.

The Wind

Scott Duncan

The wind through which
he walked
 became that which he always
hoped it would be
 that day on the prairie
when the sunlit grasses
 shimmered in their wavering
dance
He sensed his clothing as
 it fell away
and tumbled like some
 dismembered scarecrow
towards the sun.
Blowing through his pores
 the wind
separated his sinews until
 each hummed and made
the sound of coyotes in the
 twilight
and he stretched up and
 out in his ecstasy.
Then with a gust he was
 gone so many glittering
crystals
and the sound of coyotes
 was silenced
but the wind drove the
 dust before it into the eyes
of the child.

Uncle Charlie Meets a Chiropractor

Doris A. Wagar

Uncle Charlie couldn't understand, or speak one word of English.

He had a very sore back—a very conveniently sore back. He suffered loudly whenever the ladies came to call, or the priest, or when there was no beer in the cabin.

One day a new kind of doctor came to town. From the small writing on the poster he could cure anything. After much persuasion, Uncle Charlie consented to see him.

On the day of his appointment, his back was so sore he couldn't stand up straight. Aunt Martha and the boys had to lead him all the way to the doctor's office. There, much to his disgust, they made him take all his clothes off, even his long johns, which he only took off twice a year when they needed to be washed. He was given a little white gown that didn't even cover his knees. With much shoving and pushing, and a great deal of groaning, he was finally on the little table.

The doctor suddenly gave his back a twist. Uncle Charlie was horrified. He leaped from the table, pushed the doctor against the wall, and looking him right in the eye, said in perfect English, "I came here for medicine, not to fight."

Then he strode out the door, bare feet slapping, dicky shirt flapping, with back as straight as a warrior. He walked all the way home by himself.

From that day forward until the day he died, Uncle Charlie never spoke another word of English.

The Trapper

Myrna Mackey

The skinning knife flashed in his hand. With sure strokes he separated the rubbery hide from the layer of fat underneath. The shapeless mound of flesh that remained when the rich brown pelt was freed bore little resemblance to the beaver it once had been. He picked up the greasy lump and went to the door of the fur shed where the big shepherd waited patiently for her supper.

"Best dog food there is," he said, as the carcass landed with a thump on the hard packed snow outside.

The hunter has roots before recorded history. His dark-skinned face and angular features bear mute testimony to his Cree ancestors. The striking blue eyes and his Anglo-Saxon first name coupled with the French origin surname link him to this place.

He lives in Pretty Valley nestled between the Duck and Porcupine Hills. It is beautiful in summer, the big, shallow basin criss-crossed by rivers and streams. The valley is rimmed with hills covered with poplar, aspen and birch. Burned and logged-out areas are replanted.

The hunter remembers when his father went out on his trap-line for weeks at a time, travelling alone except for the dogs that pulled his sled. Things are different now. Trappers go out on snow machines, three-wheeled trikes, all terrain vehicles and four-wheeled drives. Seldom do they stay out more than a day. But some things don't change. He is wondering if any of his sons will give up high paying jobs in Alberta to come back to the Manitoba forests and the trapping. His father before him had wondered the same thing. He must wait and hope for the day his son will take over, and assure him the immortality he seeks.

Conditions are different these days. This year prices are lower, traps more expensive. There's more uncertainty and less profit. Each generation has seen big changes, but now the changes come each season. Will this way of life survive?

"I don't know," he admits. "As long as there are fur buyers, there must be trappers."

Thus, in a way, it's still the same. The beaver, the trap, the trapper and the pelt. There is still only one way to skin the beaver. The hunter holds the skinning knife in his hand, it's blade reflecting light from the naked bulb in the fur shed.

Color Blind

Myrna Mackey

What can I do to make you proud
Of the things that set one apart in the crowd?
Your jet black hair and olive skin,
In any fashion place—you're "IN".
Those who look down their pale noses
Have forgotten Alberta's prairie roses
Were your ancestors, grandmothers and kin.
It's the pale faces who've just moved in.
In spite of prejudice, just bear in mind,
The keeper of the heavenly gates, is color blind.

Queen for a Day

Genevieve Blume

My husband winced as he tugged at the heel of his boot. His knee was acting up again.

"Our neighbors had twins," he said.

"Twins!" I exclaimed. The boot fell with a dull thud on the soft carpet.

"A boy and a girl."

"Who said?"

"Oh, I was rubbering. Doc told Fred there was something wrong with the girl. It's her spine."

"Good grief," I sighed.

"Helen needed a blood transfusion, too."

We learned that Donna, the baby girl, was born with hydrocephalus, a condition known as water on the brain.

Five years later the twins arrived in my kindergarten class. Donald was bright eyed and eager, quick to find a seat, and at home in his new environment. Cheerfully and tediously, Donna inched her way forward with leg braces and the help of crutches.

As Donna and I became better acquainted, I wondered, "How can there be so many things wrong with one small person?" Besides the steel shafts in her head, she battled kidney infections and a problem with her eyes. Tunnel vision, I was told. That eliminated seatwork, crafts or looking at pictures. She could, however, enjoy stories read aloud and class singing.

It was 1974, the year of the big snow, incredible mounds of it. Snow fell regularly, followed by winds that whipped up frightful blizzards. We constantly fought the the downfalls with shovels, snow plows and bulldozers. The country roads were trails winding between the high snow banks, barely wide enough for cars to pass.

The weary winter days crept slowly by. Something had to be done about the apathy taking hold in our classroom. "A circus!" I thought. The children would love it. They would be the animals. With costumes borrowed from our local skating club, we would have bears, monkeys, tigers and even pink panthers. We could have clowns and trapeze artists as well.

They learned the circus songs, poems, and began a rhythm band. The class room walls and windows came alive with happy, mischievious, and even a few fierce animals.

The date was set for March twenty-second. Each morning the children carefully crossed out the day on our school calendar. "When will the two two day ever come?" they wanted to know.

There would be a special part for Donna. I went through the Sunday School costumes stashed away in the church basement. I found a velvet cape trimmed with tinsel. I selected the most regal looking of the wisemen's crowns. At home I packed my daughter's soft green gown worn at an Easter wedding.

The day arrived. The room buzzed with excitement. With flushed and beaming faces, the children greeted their mothers at the door.

The last act had been performed. The clowns had bounced off stage, the winsome bears had pedalled away on their tricycles and the high wire artists had bowed out graciously. The most important event was to take place.

Donna sat on her special chair. The skirt of the long dress covered her leg braces and the rich velvet set off her brown hair and eyes. The moment everyone was anticipating arrived. Handsome Corey crowned Donna queen of our circus.

Only a hint of a smile played around the corners of her mouth, but her eyes betrayed her joy. Queen for a day.

Sticky Mission

Eva Cookson

JAY D5 slid silently over the high brick wall, and dropped soundlessly to the darkness of its base. Dressed in camouflaged jump suit and black hood mask, he blended into the shrubbery.

For a few moments he crouched in the concealing shadows, only his eyes moving as he scanned the area. Satisfied that he was unobserved, he ran swiftly across the open security area to the sheltering gloom of the doorway. As he expected, the door was locked. A magnetic instrument opened it easily and he slipped inside.

The room was musty and dark, but a twitch of his hood slid a lens in front of his eyes and directed an infra-red beam ahead of him as he moved.

Quickly he searched the wall cabinets, then turned to the make-shift desk in the centre of the room. Perhaps it was a sense of quickly passing time that caused him to be careless. He pulled the desk drawer out swiftly, without examining it. There was a rattling crash as a can of pebbles tied to the back of the drawer was pulled off the desk. "Booby-trapped!' Jay D muttered. "The old can on a string trick."

"That's right, spy, the old can on a string trick. We thought somebody would be after our secret weapon plan."

Jay D turned slowly. There were four of them, all armed. No chance to get away.

"What secret plans?" he asked, trying to keep his voice steady. "I was looking for bubble gum. I can smell some in here."

"A likely story!" The voice behind the green mask was unyielding.

"Take him out to the wall. He'll talk! He knows what happens to spies and traitors.

Jay D fought desperately, but there were too many of them. He was tied to a heavy post, facing his captors, who were now armed with blow guns.

"Who paid you to steal our plans? Talk, spy."

"I was looking for bubble gum," insisted Jay D. "You'd better untie me, Dave."

"No names," the cold voice snarled. "I'm DeeJ10, remember. Now talk! Who sent you?"

Jay D's eyes were big and bright, and his feet and legs twisted frantically.

"Mom sent me to call you for dinner." Two big tears slid down Jay D's grimy five year old cheeks as he glared at his ten year old tormentors.

"You guys better untie me, right now! I gotta go to the bathroom."

Ghosts of Great Britain

Sandra Pope

A ghost welcomed me to Britain.

It was October 17, 1968. Our ship had docked in Liverpool that morning and I had checked into a hotel about ten blocks from the Edmund Station in central London. At bedtime, I slipped down into the damp sheets and shut off the light. "I lay there feeling alone in a far-off land, wondering what tomorrow would bring, when a large warm hand gripped my left arm tightly. I jerked up in bed, sweeping my right hand down my left arm time and time again, finding nothing. I tried to reason with myself. Again the hand gripped my left arm. I jumped out of bed, screaming as I ran to the door and flicked the light on. I stood frozen with fear, my eyes searching every corner of the room. There were no closet doors, no dark corners and no one in sight but me.

I thought again about the warm hand while visiting my Aunt Elizabeth in Crail, a city in Scotland between the Firth of Tay and the Firth of Forth on the shore of the North Sea.

I could find no warmth in the moist, bitter cold air which flowed through my Aunt's stone, two-storey house on the left side of the pier. Noticing my shivering, Aunt Elizabeth took me to my bedroom where the large oak door caught on the carpet as she shoved and pushed it closed until the latch clicked into its socket. Then she lit a fire in the stone fireplace and pulled two large rocking chairs alongside so we could sit talking. I told her of my experience in England, and asked, "Do you think it was a ghost?"

Elizabeth smiled. "There are many ghosts in Great Britain. Do not be afraid of them, dear," she said, as she leaned forward and patted my hand. "They are all friendly. And that reminds me, don't be afraid of the footsteps upstairs, dear," she said.

I was alarmed and curious. "What footsteps?"

Then I heard them—soft footsteps walking back and forth. I was mesmerized by the flickering shadows on the bedroom ceiling.

"She's been there for almost a century. Ever since that night when her lover was to return to her by ship. She still waits for him."

There was silence in the room except for the footsteps. Suddenly, my eyes widened as my aunt stared at the doorway. The bedroom door opened steadily, gliding over deep red carpet. Then it closed with ease and the latch clicked.

I whispered, "Was that a ghost?"

Elizabeth chuckled, "Indeed it was."

Read the Directions

Donna Cookson Martin

This morning I found myself tugging to pull open a heavy glass door, plainly marked "PUSH." I knew that within a few minutes another person would approach from the other side and push with all his strength, ignoring the sign which read "PULL."

Last Christmas morning, a young relative tore the fancy wrapping off a box to find a ten-car electric train. His father, ignoring the boy's protests, pounced on the box of tiny pieces, discarded the instruction booklet and began an hour's fruitless struggle to assemble the complex little machine.

How many Cracker cartons have you seen where the "pull and tuck in" top flap is undisturbed, while the bottom has been ripped apart?

Perhaps these actions confirm human impatience, carelessness or even illiteracy. Maybe they are reminders that natural curiosity really isn't dead. The urge for discovery and haphazard exploration has not been blunted entirely.

Why take time to read the directions when we can learn by doing? We can experience first hand the fun and frustration of discovering the "how and why" of the way things work.

Gimme a Wife

Doris A. Wagar

I think the Good Lord has things pretty well figured out. Take dying, for instance. He gave men three score and ten years to get things all messed up; then He gave women an extra ten years to straighten them out. Some women think they might have to come back several times to finish. As a liberated woman, before I come back, I am going to do some tough negotiating. I absolutely refuse to come back unless I can have a wife. I am also going to hold out for a wife who is a nurse much younger than myself.

A nurse has her days off in the middle of the week. This means she can get caught up on washing, ironing, shopping and cleaning. She won't be home on weekends to nag me about the garbage or cutting the lawn. A nurse goes to work early in the morning so she should be able to get our breakfast and pack our lunches before I have to get up. She also gets off work earlier, so she should be able to have the supper far enough along so I can sit down and relax with a cold beer in front of the TV.

I must impress on her how much more responsible my job is than hers. I sharpen pencils for an architectural firm, and if I don't work hard and get them done properly, I could cost the company millions of dollars. I must never let her think she is doing a good job. Then she might relax and not try so hard to please me.

When it comes to our vacation, there will be none of those boring shopping trips or going to the theatre. It is better for her to go camping or fishing. It is easier for her to do the washing and cooking over a campfire in the bush than in the city where she has all the conveniences. When it comes to retiring, having a much younger wife is an advantage. Not only can she keep on working, but with the kids all grown and only me to take care of, she can get a second job to fill her spare time. This way there would be plenty of money for me to do things I like.

I just had a thought. I will have to come back as a man. That is the only way I could get away with it. After all, the men have been doing it for years.

Long Life Means Work

Sharleen M. Chevraux

Women live longer than men. That's an established fact and many theories have been advanced to explain it, including the tasteless joke that women send men to their early graves by hounding them to death. I think there's a much simpler explanation.

I spent several hours last year typing an elector's list for our local enumerator. A list that looked similar to this. Doe, John—Retired; Doe, Mrs. Mary—Housewife; Jones, Mrs. Eva—Housewife; Smith, Roger—Retired; Smith, Mrs. Jane—Housewife.

Now I know these people personally. Mr. and Mrs Doe, for example, are in their 80's. He used to farm a few years back, but he sold out and they moved to town. Mrs. Jones lost her husband some 30 years ago. She lives alone in a small apartment. Roger Smith ran a store most of his life and his wife Jane was a nurse in the town's hospital. Two years ago he sold the store and she handed in her resignation. As I typed these names and almost 300 others, at least 1/4 of them with similar stories, I discovered some curious facts.

A large percentage of the voters in our area are senior citizens. The men used to be farmers, merchants, mechanics or salesmen. The women were teachers, nurses, clerks, waitresses, bank or hospital employees or simply mothers and helpmates. Many still enjoy life with their spouses but others are left alone. There were 25 widows on the list I typed, and only one widower. Why the great disparity? I believe I've found the answer.

The men who've given up their former occupations all describe themselves as retired. But not one woman does. No matter how old, how long widowed, or what profession she originally followed, every woman describes herself as a housewife. And that's the secret. Men quit when they get to a certain age. They stop working at their original jobs and don't transfer their energies to another meaningful pursuit. But women! Until the day they die they consider themselves productively employed.

I think that means something.

My Liberating Dilemma

Donna Cookson Martin

It's been a long, hard struggle—two or three thousand years, maybe more—but it looks like women's liberation is just around the corner. We've waited a long time for equality, freedom and independence and Heaven knows we deserve them, after all the meals we've cooked and the diapers we've washed. Ten years ago, when I graduated from university, I was convinced that this freedom and independence would open a whole new world for me, a world my grandmother could never have imagined.

But, for me, liberation has created more problems than it has solved. Of course, I believe in equal pay for equal work, but I've chosen to be a wife and mother. As every mother knows, her salary is paid in hugs and kisses and homemade Mother's Day cards—and they don't count toward the Canada Pension Plan.

Then too, there's that constant pressure, not just from other people, but from within myself, to have a career, to do something. Surely cooking and housework can't keep an intelligent, efficient young woman busy all day—unless, of course, she's a gourmet cook, does all the sewing for her own family and everyone else on the block, spends two days a week doing volunteer work, and keeps a huge garden. I do a bit of volunteer work, but I'm just an average sort of cook, I can't sew anything beyond split seams and buttons and I'm quite happy to leave the gardening to my husband. Yet if I pursued a career outside the home where would I find time to freeze the garden produce, comfort the friend who's having problems, or play "Mummy be a horsey," on the floor with my two year old?

Of course, I'm happy that the Pill has permitted me the freedom to choose whether or not to have children and how many. Grandmother could face each pregnancy with a happy smile or a tired sigh of resignation and, in either case, attribute it to the will of God. But I'm faced with deciding whether we can afford to raise a child, whether I should bear my children early or wait until my career is well established, whether I have the physical and psychological capability to be a good mother. And whether I am contributing unnecessarily to the population explosion. Is the burden of making such decisions really worth the freedom of choice?

If there were ever a time to delight in being a woman, that time should be now. But freedom and independence have brought with them so many dilemmas, so much responsibility. To be liberated, I feel pressed into being super-wife, super-mother, super-woman. Sometimes I feel so disenchanted with the entire liberation bag that I could cheerfully drop the whole thing and go back to being my husband's chattel. But only sometimes. Because I know that when I can struggle through these growing pains and reach the point of true and complete liberation, then I'll be able to accept myself as being just that—Me. As long as I can set and meet my own standards for liberation, I won't have to worry about other people's.

I Miss My Mind

Phyllis Alcorn

Having heard the phrase: "the mind's the first to go," I have a dreadful fear mine's already gone! I never feel any older but my actions betray me. I've become forgetful, absentminded, and vague.

Many times I have walked downstairs to the basement, then couldn't remember what I've gone for. I have dialed a telephone number, but when a voice answered, couldn't remember who I called. And why is it I can remember that we spent our third wedding anniversary picking roots, but forget to take meat out to thaw for dinner.

I've failed to add coffee to the percolator, neglected to enclose cheques in letters that say: "Please find enclosed" and hidden gifts prior to Christmas, but not found them until spring housecleaning. I've forgotten to put oatmeal in the oatmeal cookies, run countless loads of wash without putting in the clothes, and made a list so I wouldn't forget what I needed in town, then forgotten the list at home. I neglect to order fuel, phone for parts, or put a spoon in my husband's lunch bucket. And the commotion when a man has to eat his jello pudding with a jack-knife is unbelievable.

I am absent minded as well. Yesterday I opened the dishwasher filled with clean dishes, added a few dirty plates, then rewashed the entire lot. The day before I walked out of the post office and got into the wrong car! I have carried an armful of dirty laundry into the bathroom, and lifted the lid to the toilet rather than the hamper. My mind might be in neutral, but my reflexes have become quick!

I've become vague. I give the appearance of listening to my children without hearing a word they say. I nod my head, think no more about it, and the next morning at a quarter past eight, discover I have promised to supply three dozen cupcakes for a school party or agreed to chaperone a busload of youngsters on a Scout picnic.

I've known others similarly afflicted. They forget to attend meetings they've called, mislay every object they put their hands on, and fail to remember they offered their house for a Tuesday afternoon meeting, and decide to paint the living room. In one case, a husband returned home from town with a strange feeling he had forgotten something. Hours later he remembered his wife had gone to town with him.

I read a few lines the other day that described these circumstances perfectly:

> I'm satisfied with my bifocals.
> My dentures fit just fine.
> My hearing aid's adjusted,
> But, Lord, how I miss my mind!

My Secret

Doris Wagar

I am confessing a secret. I was one of the dumbest kids ever born. I was also very logical. I drove adults wild with my persistent questions. Logical and dumb is a very bad combination.

One spring morning I sat beside the slushy, melting manure pile watching the steam rise in the warm sun. When Grandma walked by I asked her what it was. She said, "It's the breath of the little calves that are going to be born this spring." Why wait for spring? The logical thing to do was dig them up now. I got down on my knees and began to dig. I hadn't got far when I was lifted from behind and marched to the house where I had to leave my clothes outside. As Grandma scrubbed me in the old wash tub she muttered crossly that it was the cow's job to dig up the calves, not mine.

We were at a sports day when a big man walked by making the loudest noise you ever heard. I wasn't impressed by his skirt, but I sure liked the noise. Mother told me, "He has a cat in the bag and it's biting its tail." The next morning I couldn't wait to get out to the barn to find the old black cat. Many tears and much iodine later, Mother told me I had better leave the bag-pipe playing to the grown-ups.

One day I came stumbling from the bush behind the barn. I was tired; my clothes were torn. My parents were very worried. Father had his "now you have done it" look on his face. "Where have you been?" he asked.

"I was looking for a baby for you. Grandma said babies came from hollow trees, and since you liked Aunt Marie's baby so much I thought you would be happy if I found one for you."

Mother gave Father a look I didn't understand and said she wasn't interested in any more babies right now. As Mother was getting me my supper she explained that babies really didn't come from hollow trees. The stork brought them. I was mad at Grandma for telling me such a story and I told her so the next time I saw her.

Have you ever heard the way wind whispers in the leaves of the trees? Grandma told me invisible people were talking to each other. I figured that if I climbed a tree and sat very still they would think I was invisible; then I could hear what they said. After lunch I climbed a tree and sat so still I was hardly breathing, except for the time I fell asleep and nearly fell. At supper time when Mother used her "this is the last time I am calling you voice," I climbed stiffly down. As I was nodding over my supper, Mother said wearily to Daddy, "Will, you really must have a talk with your daughter. She has really lost her marbles this time. She spent all afternoon roosting in a tree."

I have told you my secret with a few illustrations to prove it. Promise you won't tell my kids. They have always considered me rather clever.

Getting to the Bottom of Things

Doris M. Saunders

During the past winter, I've complained when I had to sit on a cold car seat. We all complain when we sit on the metal chairs in our church hall. Today, as I was making cushions for those chairs to avoid such a shock to our nether regions, I thought of other cold seats we used to experience.

The saddle on our old school pony's back was always cold when we clambered upon it on a below zero day. It didn't seem to get warmer as we bounced to school. The leather was so frosty we sometimes thought the inside of our legs were freezing. With cold toes, legs, seat, and hands, we felt almost frozen.

There were times when we went sliding down hills on a scoop shovel. A scoop shovel, taken from the loft on a frigid day, was never warm. To use the shovel to slide down a hill, we sat on the icy metal with the handle between our legs. We held them up in the air except when we wanted to stop, and then we were likely to get a snowy shower from dragging our heels.

At school in the spring, when puddles froze at night, we would often have what we called rubber ice. We used to slide on this rubber ice, which bent under our weight. It was fun until someone lost his footing and landed ker-plop, breaking the ice as he fell. Then screams of anguish echoed in the schoolyard as icy water soaked through clothes. For a good part of the day the unfortunate pupil sat on a cold, wet seat.

One of the coldest places to sit was the old one-holer out at the back. No inside bathroom in those days. We waited until we could wait no longer before hurriedly donning overshoes, coat, cap and mitts. We often had to wade through snow to our knees to that little snow-capped house. We probably had to brush the snow away before we lowered our bare bottoms to the frost bound seat. Oh! What a shock! It was so cold it almost burned. We never lingered, but even so, it was a long time before our bottoms warmed up.

I Love Freckles

Sandra Pope

An angel kissed my pale young brow,
And left a spot there, I know not how.
It sprouted wings, and in a week
It settled down upon my cheek.

It danced a jig to the tip of my nose,
And sprayed a cluster in zig-zag rows.
Down to my chin the little sprout crept,
Sprinkling freckles at night as I slept.

Then up it went to the lobe of my ear,
Scattering many, but I still could hear.
It wasn't too long before I was covered,
And I felt very sad, until I discovered;

For each good deed that I do,
I earned one freckle—sometimes two.
I dried my tears, and put on a smile
'Cause freckles will always be my style.

The Hills Down the Lane

Rose Marie Bos

I know the joy
of riding the hills
down the lane.
My dad taught
me to ride.
Nearly every day
the long line
of milk cows
walked the lane
in the morning;
then walked it
back at evening.
A dusty trail
it was, but as
I sat tall and proud
on my saddle pony
I didn't mind, for
my cowboy hat
shaded the
western sun
and all adversities
which came.
Now, I am not as
brave to face
the "everythings"
which cross
my dusty trail.
Yet I know
the joy of
riding the hills
down the lane.

Temper! Temper!

Eva Cookson

Perched several feet above the sidewalk on a shaky scaffold, Bill prepared to paint the letters of the faded store sign a bright red. Still three days before the Rodeo but already the street was beginning to look festive. Cowboys and performers who had come early were adding colour. Pleased with his world, Bill plunged his brush recklessly into the bright paint.

From the air base, half way between the town and the mountains, three jets rose, screaming, into the clear sky.

The man tacking flags along the edge of the next roof stopped work to watch.

"Hey, Bill," he called, "that hot-shot pilot we were talking to last night must be testing a new bird today. Look at that baby climb!"

Bill twisted around, trying to follow the bright silver speck. It had left the others behind, climbing higher and higher, towing a fluffy white jet stream.

A shriek drew his attention back to earth. He looked down into the dark eyes of a pretty brunette, dressed all in white. White, except for the angry red wound just below her shoulder. It bled down her satin shirt, her riding pants and dropped on her white buckskin boot.

Bill was horrified. How could anyone shoot the girl? And why was she looking at him? He had no gun, only a paintbrush still drooling slow drops, not of blood, but paint. Red paint!

"I'm sorry, miss. I'm sorry. I'll get it cleaned. I didn't mean...I wasn't think...I was watch ..."

Bill couldn't get his tongue untangled. It didn't matter. The girl wasn't listening.

"Imbecile!" she screamed. "Nit-wit! You...you...irresponsible jackass!"

Far above, the silver bird had reached the peak of its flight, turned, and started down a long, smooth, screaming slide, gaining momentum all the way.

It reached the speed of sound, thundered through and started to climb again.

The girl stamped her foot.

BOOM!

Windows shattered along the street, bottles exploded, merchandise spilled off shelves. Bill's makeshift scaffold broke loose from the wall and slowly collapsed, dumping him in the street. He sprawled beside his paint bucket in a red puddle of paint.

Bill looked hurt.

"Damn," he said sadly. "I said I was sorry."

A Dairyman's Dilemma

Blanche McGowan

When you get up at 5:30 every morning, 7 days a week, 365 days a year, and sometimes work until midnight, you live on a dairy farm. It is a challenge. You are milkmaid, chore girl, housewife, mother, midwife, and mind-reader, and still get yelled at for no reason when things go wrong, especially if a cow kicks a pail over.

It was spring and that meant calving time. Spot was due to have her calf but she was taking her own time.

Bob said, "Something must be wrong or she's going to have twins. We'd better keep an eye on her."

Finally the day came when Spot acted queerly and wandered off by herself. We got her into the old barn, our maternity ward.

"You and Goldene will have to help me," Bob said. "The calf isn't coming right and we'll have to take it." He got all the necessary things ready, a rope, paper towel, and a small chain.

Spot wasn't happy to have us around while she was trying to have her calf. Bob got the chain on the calf's legs and fastened the rope to it.

"You and Goldene pull when I tell you," he said and handed me the rope. "Now pull."

We did. The rope broke and sent me flying. I hit the door which swung out. I slid right under it and landed on the half frozen cow pies outside. The door slammed behind me. I was stunned and couldn't move.

The door opened. Bob and Goldene stood there laughing, not helping me, just laughing. Between laughs they finally asked, "Are you hurt?" They helped me up, still laughing.

"I don't see anything funny." I wasn't really hurt, only my pride. We went back into the barn. Spot was licking her calf. All was well.

The dairy business has its own reward.

To the Groundhog

Eva Cookson

Up through the grass-roots slyly sneaking,
For your shadow shyly seeking.
Is the sky dark and grey,
Or is it a bright and sunny day?
What does the weather for you choose?
Early to rise, or six weeks to snooze?
The sky is clear, old sleepy head,
So yawn and scratch and go back to bed.

Beware of Left-Overs

Phyllis Alcorn

I opened my 'fridge door this morning and nearly got mugged before I could slam it shut again. Waiting for my pulse to quit racing, I told myself I didn't believe in reincarnation — at least not from left-overs.

Then what could have been in the refrigerator so long it had grown legs or sprouted wings? Mentally, I tried to tick off the possibilities. Was it that dab of sweet and sour sauce left over from last week's gourmet dinner? Perhaps that wizened lump of gravy I saw curling away from the sides of a saucepan four days ago? The culprit couldn't have been there TOO long. I distinctly remember cleaning the refrigerator after the last power failure. Now, how long ago was that?

I mustered up my courage and opened the door a crack. Nothing happened. Gritting my teeth, I methodically began checking items:
New: one loaf of bread, a tin of ravioli, and four black bananas—
none of which should be in refrigerator
Used: six partially emptied salad dressing bottles—three coleslaw,
three French; one juice pitcher and two large covered bowls
—both empty and one half-full carton of cream—extremely
sour.
Left-overs: a garage sale of bowls containing a table-spoon of
mashed potatoes, a dozen wrinkled peas, a spoonful of
dried-up rice and one hamburger pattie, green at edges.

Out of that entire menagerie nothing moved, or looked like it had moved for quite some time. Next, I checked the crispers. They held an over-ripe tomato—soft; three Christmas oranges—hard; a partially-used onion in open plastic bag—strong; a rotten, brown pile I think was once a head of lettuce—limp; a corsage from New Year's Eve—past re-cycling; a single unpeeled potato—sprouting; a rolled up package—contents unknown; a jar containing Junior's biology experiment

— also sprouting; a shrivelled wiener, one slice of raw bacon and a bad smell.

I checked contents in the refrigerator door: butter keeper: several chunks and lumps, all of which should be pensioned off. They are in various stages of growth and could supply enough penicillin for an entire hospital. Door shelf: three jars jelly—one half-full (looks like raspberry); one without lid, or jelly; a bottle of relish and one of suppositories left over from teenager's babyhood.

As I kneel to check the bottom shelf, I catch sight of a slight movement from the back of the top shelf, extreme rear. I think fast. Before I phone the exterminators, I'll leave the door ajar for half an hour.

Star Watch

Eva Cookson

Weary and wakeful, I watched a star,
As wide awake as I,
Follow a set and lonely path
Across a spangled sky.
Snail paced, it crossed my window,
Slow creeping, pane by pane,
To be lost at last behind the wall.
Tomorrow it will come again.

Walking Through Sunlight

Scott Duncan

The poplar trees were
    sending out
floating tree-clouds
which cast their shadows on
the sidewalk
upon which he walked
through sunlight
and he noticed how these
    shadows
seemed to float darkly past
indistinct and vague when
    the tree-cloud
was closer to the sun
well-defined when the tree
    cloud
was closer to the ground
and he also noticed how his
    own shadow
became such an increasingly
    poor
representation of himself
as he too floated
closer to the sun.

AUGUSTANA UNIVERSITY COLLEGE
LIBRARY.

My Home in Papua, New Guinea

Doris Likness

The poinciana tree, a vision of flaming blossoms, shades the laundry area at the rear of our small house. Below, the spikey pineapple plants invite inspection, while the great drooping leaves of banana plants beyond reveal clusters of fruit soon ready for the knife. I look at the initialled pawpaws with a smile, the work of students who had recently weeded our yard. Suddenly, a tiny breeze wafts the fragrant perfume of our frangipani flowers. I sniff delightedly. I bend down to feel the soft petal of a rose and to admire the huge hibiscus blossoms on a nearby bush.

As I stroll out the gate where great coconut palms rear their stately fronds, I hear native voices. Soon a little family comes into view. The mother, laden with a huge bilum of garden produce, the strap bound over her head, struggles painfully along. A toddler straddles her shoulders. Her man strides ahead, unencumbered except for an axe he idly carries. A small boy trots beside him, only a shell necklace adorning his nakedness. I call a greeting "Apinun! Apinun!" The father responds: "Apinun, missy" His wife turns her head with effort and smiles. She is proud, so I've been told, to be able to bear the great load under which she toils. "No wonder," I muse, "these poor women are worn out before they reach their middle years."

When the tropical darkness falls like a veil and a great full moon rides high in the heavens and the stars appear so warm and close, I gaze in awed delight. The gently soughing palms are silvery in the moonlight while below among the bushes fireflies flit. I can't refrain from exclaiming; "Oh, how beautiful!" The young student seeing me safely to my door replies: "I don't think it's beautiful." A familiar scene for him; an unearthly vision of loveliness for me.

My Secret Place

Sharleen M. Chevraux

A trail, half hidden by prairie wool, winds through poplar trees, raspberry bushes and silver willow. It leads to a forgotten meadow where purple violets, yellow buffalo beans and tiny white daisies bloom— where the breeze blows gently and the deer frolic and play unseen.

I love my secret place. I went there once just after a shower when the waist high grass along the trail was still sticky wet, when rain spattered my face from quivering leaves overhead. The air was fresh and clean and smelled of spring. I plucked a branch of a silver willow bush and rolled it around in my hand, and sniffed at the tangy sweetness of it. A rabbit hopped from the undergrowth and stopped to look at me, his nose twitching with frightened curiosity. I was afraid to breathe for fear he'd leave but he decided to stay. The two of us sat and enjoyed the sun as it peeped through the clouds overhead and dappled the path with golden light.

My meadow has a buffalo wallow—a small dip in the hollows of the land. On a hot dry day when the heat waves shimmer, I can almost see those shaggy beasts, rolling and pawing and kicking their feet in dusty ecstasy. They came here once to graze and sleep, and their musky odor must have filled the air just as their snorts and bellows did. They vanished long ago and silence reigns in their place. Almost silence. A robin sings and a bluebird calls. From somewhere near a loon laughs at her mate. A gopher whistles and the prairie wool rustles as a coyote slinks by. A sudden squawk and a ruffled grouse dies, her death just out of my sight.

There's nothing can beat my secret place when twilight comes in the fall. The leaves on the trees turn orange and brown and carpet my world. The robins and bluebirds are gone. High overhead, honking V-s head south. Now the deer venture out from the trees and bound through the ripening grass. I've watched them at play and I've seen them stand still and sniff at the strengthening breeze. Catching my scent, they twitch their tails, give a leap and are gone.

When next I go to my secret place, snowflakes are fluttering down. They are cold and they land on my face and I lick them with joy. They transform the branches so bare and forlorn and blanket the meadow with white. They are silent and soft and I am alone, until a rabbit hops by leaving his tracks in the snow. A deer peers through the bare branches of a nearby tree. A bluejay utters his harsh cry and a chickadee chirps from his perch on a bush. I laugh and feel happy.

There's a little trail, now hidden with snow, that leads to a secret place that I know.

Grandma's House

Molly Shier

Warm dusk invaded the still hallway. The sun's rays spread across it, fingers of light in dancing streams through the glass windows in the heavy oaken door. I pushed it open and caught the fragrances that endeared this house to me; old carpets, brittle wallpaper; cleanliness; the faint hint of cigar smoke. As I walked towards the kitchen, the heart of this house, I could smell my grandmother's homemade soup bubbling on the stove. The hall floor sighed as I walked across it. The kitchen's expanse of shining blue linoleum greeted me. Images of myself as a child, playing solitaire, or painting pictures on the squeaky kitchen table were happy remembrances. This room, this house, always wraps me in a glow of warmth. I settled into a kitchen chair wanting to daydream of my childhood when grandmother's world held out comforting arms to her favorite grandchild.

Dream Home

Irene Findlay

Over the years my husband and I dreamed of building a bermed, energy efficient house. Clare drew up a plan of his own design which required a piece of land with a hill site. By 1979 land prices reached a peak of one thousand dollars per acre. Our bermed house would have been just a dream, except for our pioneering spirit. We were not to be daunted and explored other types of energy efficient housing.

Research on insulation values and air infiltration was done as early as 1930 in Saskatoon. A Canadian Passive Solar house was first designed by Keith Funk of Concept Construction. Dave Larsen of Bentley built one of the earliest Passive Solar houses in Alberta. He used the plans from Concept.

Our plans for a 1080 square foot house with a finished basement were drawn up by the same company. We built in Sedgewick where serviced lots were most reasonable.

We purchased the building requirements: insulation, double glaze windows for a southern exposure, two sets of mylar curtains, electric base heaters, a wood-burning stove. The air-exchanger we made and the trombe wall was poured out of concrete on the site. We began building on the second of May and moved in on the twelfth of December, with some of the inside still to finish.

The total cost of the house built in 1980 was fifty-two thousand dollars. This included the solar components and extra insulation which were about ten percent of the total building cost.

Our life style changed considerably with wood to haul, saw and carry inside, ashes to carry out and a chimney to clean. It hardly seemed like progress, but my husband assured me we would enjoy it. "Like pioneering," he said. It does seem worth it now with no high gas bills winter after winter.

Considering the poorly insulated houses we have lived in before, where even our house plants froze on the kitchen counter, this is a wonderful break through in air-tight housing. We find it ideal for the cold climate of Western Canada.

There will be improvements and newer ways of designing these houses. Our house will be dated within a short time, but we feel it is a major step in the furtherance of the use of solar energy. Our house is comfortable, attractive, warm and energy efficient.

It is our dream home.

The Lure of the Tent

Sharleen M. Chevraux

"A white tent pitched by a glassy lake,
Well under a shady tree,
Or by rippling rills from the grand old hills,
Is the summer home for me."
(Canadian Camping Song, 1893)

We gave tenting up several years ago in favor of a trailer with its own toilet and other, less necessary, luxuries. But I sometimes wonder if it was a poor trade. Sleeping under canvas has a charm and delight that no trailer can replace.

I remember my first tenting holiday, taken with my sister and my parents when I was ten, and the sense of adventure with which I crawled into the tent at night to undress by the beam of a small flashlight.

Excitement more than cold made me shiver as I slipped into a sleeping bag and zipped myself into cozy warmth. The delicious strangeness of it all—the fresh coolness of the air on my face and head; the flapping of the canvas in a slight breeze; the eerie calls and snufflings and rustlings of the night just inches away. And the good sleep.

Waking up in a tent to the dewy fresh smell of morning is a joy, especially when the sun is shining with the promise of a beautiful day. Dressing in the confines of a tent is awkward, but as a child I didn't care and as an adult, the smell of wood smoke and bacon cooking over an open fire soon made me forget the scramble for slightly damp clothes and the bumps of the head on the tent pole as I pulled them on.

The smell of coffee boiling on a campsite stove is an invitation to tenting neighbors to drop by and visit. Many new friendships have begun that way. My parents still correspond with people we met on that holiday when I was ten. And my husband still uses the recipe for beer pancakes given him by an older couple from Washington State whom we met on our honeymoon.

But for me, tenting was less about people and more about sensations. The somnolent heat of a tent in the afternoon of a mid-summer day. The smell of hot canvas. Or the sound of rain drops plop, plopping in the middle of the night, joining with the soughing of wind in branches. Reaching out with a finger to trace a raindrop's path down the canvas and feeling the water come dripping through. Watching the flickering campfire through the tent walls and dreaming in the shadows.

On the other hand, I don't miss the long walks to the little house in the trees, especially at night. And I really like the softness of my trailer bed. So would I go back to the tent? Well...maybe sometime.

Farewell Blue and Gold

Lynne Bevington

This is it. I close my locker door and stagger down the hall with my books. I pass the principal's office.

"Goodbye, Mrs. Lasser," I say, poking my head into the small room.

"You're going now?" she asks.

"Yes, this is it," I reply, and shift the heavy books in my arms.

"Can I help you with those?"

"No, I can do it."

I've wanted to strike out on my own for a long time. It's just that twelve years of memories are hard to leave behind.

I continue down the hall, glancing in vacant classrooms. The social room, the English room, the science lab.

I remember our squeamish groans the first time we did a disection in biology...

As I pass the washroom, memories of hiding in the cubicles to smoke, of mid-morning gossip sessions and mirror checks, of private confidences shared with friends, all come pouring back. I want to open the door once again and see them all—combing their hair, blowing bubbles— but because I know they're not behind the door anymore, I reluctantly pass by.

I take one last look at the home ec room—the place where Jan and I burned those bran muffins; where Karol and I made chilli but forgot the chili powder; where in grade ten we had a fashion show in which we modelled our first sewing efforts. The place where I not only had fun, but learned how to take criticism, learned not to get upset when things went wrong, and where I learned most about being a woman. It played a big part in my growing up.

Here I am. The end of the hall. All that's left is one more door. Twelve years of my life completed. Finished. I never did go to the principal for the strap. I used to be proud of that fact—a perfect record—but, I don't know, I think I'd like another shot at being a little hellian.

My feet have stopped moving. After twelve years of waiting and yearning for the moment when I could get out of this brick building of boredom, I find myself wishing I was back in grade one—that first day when big sisters had to sit with bawling kids who wet their pants and screamed when Mommy had to go. Kids that finally got to know each other, started making friends, playing together at recess, changing friends, mocking new kids and crying over a thousand-and-one trivialities. Then starting to notice the opposite sex as somthing other than "yucky," shyly kissing under the mistletoe at the Junior High dances, dating and alas, Graduating. Some of those "kids" are now mothers, are dropouts, or have moved away. Three have died. Some will stay here, and some, like me, will go. We'll never all be together again.

This is it. Even after twelve years of preparing, I'm not sure if I'm ready. How can I get through the day without hearing Mrs. McMullen's raspy voice go through the roll call, or watch Mr. Gutten's face turn red when discussing sexual reproduction in biology?

There comes a time when you gotta let go.

I Remember

Jennifer Davidson

...getting stuck in the mud and Mom's angry scowl
when she pulled me out

...tree climbing and tree houses. Mom was sure we'd
fall and hurt ourselves.

...rafting and swimming and Mom worrying about
whether we'd drown.

...begging for music lessons and Mom driving forty
miles every week to take me.

...joining clubs and Mom taking on leadership roles so
that the clubs wouldn't die.

...breaking Mom's best china. She said it didn't matter
but I knew it did.

...being sick and Mom there to look after me.

...phoning Mom from thirty miles away and asking her
to come get me. She came.

...wanting to finish a new dress for a special occasion
and Mom helping me get it finished.

...wanting to go to a dance, to a party, to a show or to a
meeting and always being able to get the car.

...the night my boyfriend dumped me, the day my
best friend and I fought, the problems of getting
along in this world, and Mom always being there to
listen.

...wanting advice and getting it. Wanting to make my
own decision and being left to make it.

...being mad at her and yelling at her and loving her at
the same time.

Determination

Rose Marie Bos

I robbed you
again this morning,
of maternal instincts
life's fullness
its magical powers.

You tried desperately
but in vain
with dry grass, leaves
sage boughs, mud
bits of string
shaping a nest
frantically framing
my front door lamp.

But there will be
no tiny eggs laid
no gaping babies
eagerly begging worms
no fledglings
spreading open wings
soaring deep blue skies.

How determined
as I tear down
you rebuild
bursting with excitement
enduring hardships
you cannot win
unless, of course,
I choose to let you
rule my front door
at swallow time.

All About You Dad

Sandra Pope

For the past three Father's Days I have wanted to walk into the countryside alone, and find a hilltop beneath the clouds where I could sit and talk to you, Dad.

When I realized you were leaving us, I had a sudden urge to know much more about you; your passage to Canada at age 14, and why you came to an Alberta farm to work. I want to know more about grandfather, but all you ever told me about was the day he shot your pet bird.

I want you to know that it never did bother me that we didn't have a car. I got pleasure in riding your bike. I will never forget the day you put my little body upon that big high seat and gave me a push.

I remember when you got so tired watching a neighbor whip his dog, that you took the whip out of his hand, and took the dog home with you. Tippet became a part of our family.

How old were we when George started the house on fire and burned almost everything—even the little crib you made for my dolls?

You were so worried when George was run over by a city bus. The year he was in hospital, I hardly saw you—what with your visiting him and working overtime to pay the bills. If a door said "No Admittance" or "Do Not Enter," you said George would wheel himself through the doors to see why. It was a wonderful day when George came home and we were a family again; but not for long. Uncle Ray's tractor tires fell on his legs and broke them the following week.

You used to get mad at George, too. First when he siphoned gas from a neighbor for that $5.00 Nash of his, and then when he stole Christmas tree bulbs from yards in the neighborhood. You were so scared when the police came and put George's name in their little black book. You were sure that George would turn out to be a hoodlum. You were surprised when George became a Probation Officer, and now he almost has a degree in Economics at the University of Alberta. Yes Dad—George! That little nerd who failed Grade 7 and quit in the middle of Grade 10.

When I was about eight years old, I was terrified of dying, and being put into the dark ground. You explained to me that I would not be alone—that there would be a kind, wonderful Father waiting for me in Heaven. And Heaven you said, is such a wonderful place. There are swimming pools filled with soda pop, ice cream and candy.

I shall never forget the look on your face when I received my first paycheque and paid you $40 for room and board. I thought maybe you would stop buying your clothes and shoes at the Army and Navy. Little did I know that you socked away the extra money for Mom, in case you were not always around to look after her.

What does a grown daughter do to become friends with a father? I used to ask you to do my income tax. I could have learned myself, but I felt that was one way we could do something together. I would give you fishing tackle as a reward—usually the hooks I had lost during our last trip out.

One of the best lessons I learned from you was—"It doesn't matter who makes the mistake: the only important thing is to rectify it!" It was from that lesson that I grew up without blaming and judging others. That lesson has backfired too. The children think their Mom can fix everything. Whenever I came to you with a problem, your advice would be simply to "forget it!" I never could do that. I had to scream, cry and try to run away, and then forget it.

You would be so proud of your grandchildren. Tricia is ten, and she is going to be tall like you. Even though Jody is only eight, he looks just like you, except that he has lots of hair. He will have the huge hands you had that practically took the skin off my back when you bathed me at a young age, and that threw that young boyfriend across the room when he told me to "shut-up."

I still write poetry and stories, and have all your creative writing in my drawer. I read it now and then, and fantasize what it must have been like working for Aircraft Repair during the War. I remember the

ending of your lovely poem to Mom - "But the best gift I ever knew,
Was when before the Minister, I heard you said "I do"!

The day you left, Dad, we could scarcely get Tippet up the back steps.
She moaned constantly at the thought of never going for a walk with
you again. She dug a huge hole through the living room carpet, and
from then on, she would not eat. We finally put her to sleep, but we
didn't cry. We knew that she wanted to be with you, where the two of
you would again go for evening walks, hopefully out to the countryside hilltops, beneath the clouds.

Father

Violet M. Copeland

My father wove his own philosophy
Into the sturdy pattern of his day.
He read no tomes of child philosophy
But let his theories pervade his ways.
Those quiet ways we followed in his wake
Down the plowed field whose fragrant earthy scent
Comes back with clear remembrance from my youth
With thoughts of summer rain and deep content.

He hummed a wordless tune at every task.
It often lulled the youngest child to rest
Sprawled close in trusting weariness against
The broad protection of his sturdy chest.
His tones were low; still lower when he spoke
An urging or an absolute command;
His tastes were simple; not beyond his means
His was the calm, ripe wisdom of the land.

Please God,
I Want a Papa

Doris Likness

I take the short cut home from school, through a neighbour's yard and down the back alley. I bound up the steps into our kitchen with its big black stove in one corner. There is no one in sight. I go down the hall and listen. I can hear Mama's sewing machine humming away. "Mama, Mama, I'm home!" I call up the winding stairs. The sewing machine stops.

"I'm busy, Doris. You may have a cookie, then practise your music lesson."

I run back down the hallway and into our pantry just off the kitchen. The big cookie jar is on the bottom shelf. I choose the biggest cookie I can find. As I munch its chocolate goodness, I walk through the swinging door into the dining room, passing our big table and the leather couch against the wall, handy for an extra visitor. I open the sliding doors into our sitting room. How lovely Mama's geraniums look in front of the big east window! I like this room with its pretty sofa and two fat chairs. Our big piano is against one wall. As I finish my cookie, I study the picture of Papa above the piano in its beautiful gold frame. Mama says I look like him. I'm glad.

I remember when Papa was very sick in bed. I was only five. I said to Mama, "Is Papa going to die?" Mama had hugged me tight, tears rolling down her face. She said: "No, oh no!" But my Papa did die. I remember Mama taking me and Walter, who is a year older than I am, to see him in his coffin. Then from our front window we watched men carry it out. Mama stayed with us. She was too sick and sad to go along. Besides our new little baby sister needed very special care. She was so tiny that Uncle Rex called her Buster, just for fun. Her real name is Violet. My two middle sisters are Audrey next to me, and Sis. Sis's real name is Olive, like Mama's.

As I turn the page for my music lesson, I hear footsteps on our wooden walk. Excited, I peek out the window. It's Uncle Horace! I fly out the door and down the steps into his arms. My dear, handsome Uncle Horace is here. He gives me a big kiss and taking my hand we go into the house together. "Mama, Mama," I call once again. "Uncle Horace is here!"

Mama comes to the top of the stairs, smiles and says, "Hello, Horace. Help yourself to a drink. I'll be down in a few minutes." Mama keeps a bottle of something for Uncle on the top shelf of our pantry. I watch him happily as he pours his drink into a glass. We go into the sitting room and Uncle stretches out in a big chair. I love my French Canadian uncle with his funny way of talking. I love his kind, brown eyes and moustache with two points. I love to hear stories about his big family in Quebec. Mind you, he has eighteen brothers and sisters. He hasn't even seen them all, because he left home when he was only sixteen.

My Uncle Horace is a provincial policeman now and wears a khaki uniform. Before, he was a Mountie and then he wore a red uniform. Not long ago a sad thing happened. Auntie Daisy died and their new little baby, too. Of course, my Mama and Auntie Vi had to help the family for a few days. Phoebe is eighteen and will have to leave her job at the post office to keep house for the family. Uncle Horace has seven children. I feel very sorry for them. I cry when I think about it.

Mama comes down. She wants to talk to Uncle Horace. I won't have to practise my music now. I can read my book instead. My family calls me a "book-worm." I go upstairs because I have a tiny secret corner on our big balcony where I can be alone. Audrey and Sis are playing dolls in the big bedroom we share together. I have to go through Walter's room where the balcony door is. A curtain separates his room from ours. When we are all in bed at night, Walter pulls back the curtain so he can hear my story, too. I make it up as I go along. It's usually very sad. Soon my sisters are all crying. Then Mama comes in to see what's going on. Audrey and Sis sob: "Mama, make Doris stop telling such sad stories!" Mama scolds me gently, pulls the curtain between our rooms and we all settle down to our dreaming.

Out on the balcony, curled up in my special corner, I find I cannot read. I just think and think. My cousins have no mother. We have no father. I work out a wonderful plan. Why couldn't Uncle Horace and his family come to live with us! I jump up happily. "I'll ask Mama if it wouldn't be a good idea." I run through Walter's room and downstairs. Mama is in the pantry. When I whisper my splendid idea to her, she looks at me so funny. Then she says, "Why, Doris, you know our house isn't big enough for two families."

A couple of weeks later, Phyllis, my cousin, comes for a visit with her Papa, Uncle Horace. We are the same age. Nine. We always have a secret talk in my corner of the balcony. I hug her and say, "I wish you were my sister. I wish your Papa would marry my Mama. I haven't had a Papa for such a long time."

Phyllis' brown eyes sparkle. "Oh, wouldn't that be fun!"

"What do you suppose we can do about it, Phyllis?"

After a thoughtful minute she says, "We can pray. She crosses herself like she does before she eats. I don't do this but my cousin goes to a different church where they learn to do these things. "Please, dear God, may we have Auntie Olive for our Mama? Amen."

It is my turn. "Dear God, I want a Papa so badly. You have my own Papa in heaven with you. Please let Uncle Horace marry my Mama. Amen."

We run happily downstairs and do a little skipping before supper. After we've eaten, Phyllis goes to help Mama put Buster to bed. My sisters are upstairs, too, and Walter is shutting up the chickens in our backyard. Uncle Horace is smoking his pipe and reading the paper in a big armchair. I wonder if God will mind if I give Him a little help. I feel so shy I almost start to cry. I stand at his side and whisper, "Uncle Horace, do you like being a Papa?"

He puts his paper down and holds his pipe in one hand. "Of course, little one. Why do you ask?"

"How would you like to have a bigger family?" I hold my breath as I wait to hear what he will say.

"Well, no, not right now." I begin to cry a little.

"Oh, wouldn't you like to be my Papa?" I sob.

He hugs me tight with his empty hand. "Dear little girl, I know you miss your Papa. Do you think I could be your Papa-Uncle? Then you can talk to me like a Papa any time you wish. Isn't that the best way?"

"Maybe," I agree doubtfully. I smile through my tears. He squeezes me again, puts his pipe in his mouth and picks up his paper.

I am sad that my dream cannot come true. I walk into the hall and lean against the stairpost. I wonder how Phyllis will feel when I tell her. I hear noisy voices upstairs. Maybe Mama is right after all. Our house just isn't big enough for twelve children. What would we do for beds? Even for chairs?

My Son

Sharleen M. Chevraux

He infuriates me
sometimes
this son of mine
grown so tall,
so independent,
so reckless.
I want to say to him
No!
As I did
when he was small.
You mustn't.
You'll get hurt.
But he looks at me
with exasperation
Oh, Mother!
and then defiance
You can't stop me.
And I swallow my anger,
turn it back to fear.

The New Baby

Marge Boutin

"Marge."

I struggled to awaken. I turned my head and through half-open eyes saw Denis beside my bed, a tender expression on his face.

"Marge, I saw her."

"You did?" I mumbled.

"Yes, when they wheeled her into the nursery, I saw her. Marge—she is pretty. I thought all new-born babies were supposed to be red and wrinkled, but she's not. Her skin is smooth and pink."

I smiled up at him. His words were like a balm on my weary body. I felt I could sleep for days. Sleep—that's what I wanted now. I closed my eyes and did not hear him leave.

***

I opened my eyes. It was very quiet and it took a moment to remember where I was and to realize what I was doing there.

A short, white-haired nurse with a beaming face bustled into the room and a cheery, grandmotherly voice interrupted my thoughts.

"Hello, dearie. How are you? My, but you've got a little sweetheart. She's been as good as gold. Asleep since they brought her in."

I tried to sit up. "I haven't seen her yet."

"Oh, my, we can't have that. Here I'll help you up and then I'll get her."

I couldn't think while the nurse was gone. I didn't know what to expect. The nurse came back into the room and with a sense of shock I saw that the pink bundle she held wasn't quite the length of her hand to her elbow. She laid the sleeping baby beside me and left. I held my breath and didn't move. I couldn't take my eyes off that perfectly formed little face, the round chin, the tiny pink mouth, the wee button of a nose, the two half circles of her closed eyes, the smooth brow, and the fine black hair lying close to her head. Denis was right. She was pretty! I could not get my fill of looking. Tears welled up in my eyes and I tried to swallow the lump in my throat. I could not believe that she was mine. I took a couple of deep breaths to slow my pounding heart.

At last I made a move. Tentatively I reached out and touched a tiny hand that was rolled up into a ball. The hand jerked open. The reaction caught me by surprise and I laughed shakily. The eyes opened and seemed to be searching for the source of that sound. Such dark eyes! Could they really see me? Again I touched her hand and she curled it around my finger. I smiled. What a strong little grasp she had. Five pink fingers each ending in a wee fingernail. It was wonderful and a tear crept out of the corner of my eye and rolled down my cheek. My baby.

A Son Is...

Rose Marie Bos

A Son is: sunshine through curtains of rich blue
lace...a sleeping angel with dimpled
face...diapers and bottles at dawn's first
light...prayers beside a crib at night...teddy
bears, scattered toys, tip-toeing on a
stair...lullaby's sung in a rocking chair...tasks
left undone, a clothes line in a breeze...hugs and
kisses and grandmas to please...baths, bedtime
stories, dreams of fright...flanelette pyjamas on
a wintry night...clothes tossed in closets with
empty hooks...crayon-marked walls of heroes and
crooks...bruises and hurts mended by
kisses...shrieks of delight at favorite
dishes...puzzles and models with crooked
wheels...kites in springtime, a dog at his
heels...smiles and tears wrapped up
together...band-aids, picnics and rainy
weather...cyclone-tossed bedroom—'Don't Disturb'
on the door...muddy boot tracks on a clean kitchen
floor...chocolate milk and pink
lemonade...munching on warm-baked cookies just
made...tummy-aches, fevers, thermometers,
fears...stories read over and over for
years...endless questions and growing
pains...pockets—a treasure chest of the
unexplained...tousled hair, ragged blue
jeans...clean ironed shirts, ripped at the
seams...baseball, bicycles, anything that
roars...jam and peanut buttered cupboard
doors...all special days he never misses..."Mom, I
love you's" with shy sticky kisses...gathering bouquets
by the hours of Mother's Day weeds—he calls flowers.

The Encounter

Maurice Shank

He was seated, reading, the first time I saw him. Grey, irritated eyes glanced up and returned to their reading. There was the minutest nod of acknowledgement and then, save an occasional rustle of paper, nothing.

It seemed a long time after that before I thought to inquire if I might smoke. I was answered with a violent rustle of papers and another nod. Uncertain about this response, I decided to refrain. There we sat, the two of us, he engrossed in his newspaper and I in silence. It seemed an eternity.

Wanting desperately to end the silence, I began to speak about the weather. I spoke of weather in past, present and future tenses. Emboldened by what I thought to be an encouraging nod from behind the papers, I started again. I spoke of children, pets and politics. It was a most disjointed parade of words, yet I was pleased with the voice sounds, even though they were my own.

The one-sided conversation continued. I spoke of professions and described my own. At this point, the paper went down, was carefully folded and set aside. For the first time, I became aware of intent grey eyes set in a handsome, angular face framed by well-tended greying hair. We studied one another for a long moment, and then he spoke to me.

I sometimes wonder which of my words had penetrated his defenses and brought down that wall of paper. I wonder what caused him to surrender his silence and reach out. I have no answers. However, we have become friends, this grey-eyed silent man and I.

Playmates

Sharleen M. Chevraux

We met by chance one day in the city. I looked at him curiously, seeing the few threads of grey, noting the heavier frame and the rounder face. We went for coffee together, awkwardly, unused to the people we had become.

"Do you remember "Kick the Can?" He grinned at me, and suddenly I saw the boy I knew.

I had crouched behind the hedge and peered through its tangled branches at him as he stood beneath the street light, arms flung across his eyes. The branches scratched at my face and caught in my hair as he chanted, "...eight, nine, ten. Here I come, ready or not."

Excitedly I watched while he hesitated for a moment, then plunged into darkness across the road, searching. When he was gone, I wriggled free and began a low crouching run to the dark hollows of the ditch. Halfway there I stopped, listening to the rustling of leaves in the hedge behind me. Suddenly there was a muffled groan, then muted whispers—then silence again. I reached the ditch and flung myself low among the prickly grasses and weeds. A sharp stone dug into my thigh and I wedged it away with my leg.

Footsteps thudded down the road past me and I peeked over the grassy bank to see him tag another girl as she squealed in mock anger. Someone darted out of the hedge and reached the shadows of a large tree. A girl dropped heavily into the ditch beside me. I felt her groping hand touch my shoulder.

"Where is he now?" she hissed. "Down by the hospital?"

"No, he's coming back." I grabbed her sweater and pulled her down again.

The street light at Sorken's corner was home base for the twenty or thirty of us who gathered nightly, and underneath that lamp post was the old jam can that we had to kick to win the game. The post was only a short distance away but he could run awfully fast and there was no point in trying to beat him there unless he wasn't looking in our direction.

"Okay! Come on," she whispered gleefully.

He turned and was running towards two figures slipping across the open street. Jumping to my feet, I scrambled after her toward the lamp post. Someone was pounding down the road behind me. Someone else dashed in front of me. Suddenly the corner was alive with kids—all racing for the jam can. I reached it first. But just as I got there, a leg shot out. The can clunked over and a voice chortled, "I beat you! I beat you!"

Without thinking I said, "You always do."

His laugh brought me back to the present and I grinned at him over the rim of the mug.

"I remember," I said.

Double Vision

Eva Cookson

Wendy sat bolt upright, her hands gripping the covers convulsively. Her feet were braced desperately against the foot of the bed. Fear drenched her body with cold sweat.

Headlights blazed before her eyes. Tires screeched. Metal shrieked as it buckled and ripped. Glass exploded.

There was pain, terrible pain. Then came the smell of smoke and dust and the salty, bitter taste of blood. Quiet came. The airfield beacon continued to sweep the clouds. Only laboured breathing, the crackle of the growing fire and the far off sound of a siren, disturbed the night.

Realization and horror came to the girl simultaneously. She felt the increasing heat of the fire and watched the flashing beacon fade and dim, until the blackness closed down and even the pain was gone.

"Denny, no! No, Denny! Don't go!" she screamed over and over. Then her mother was there, shaking her.

"Wendy, Wendy, wake up. You are having a nightmare. Denny isn't home yet."

"Denny isn't coming home," said the girl dully. "He's had an accident out by the airport."

"You've had a bad dream," her mother insisted. "Come to the kitchen. We'll have a hot drink and wait for him."

"I'll get dressed, " replied the girl, in a far away voice. "We'll be going to the hospital when the police call."

"I'll put the kettle on. We'll talk about your dream when you are wide awake."

"I was not dreaming! I saw it. I heard it and I felt it. You'll see!" The girl was crying quietly now as she fumbled for her clothes.

Her mother watched her with a growing sense of fear.

"Mrs. Cameron? This is Cpl. Country of the RCMP. There has been an accident. I'm afraid your son is seriously injured. A patrol car will pick you up in a few minutes to take you to the hospital. The driver can tell you all we know." After a moment he spoke again, hesitantly. "Would you know whether he was alone? He kept saying, "Wendy, I'm sorry. Let me go, Wendy!" but we couldn't find anyone else at the scene."

Mrs. Cameron could not keep her voice steady...

"Thank you...we'll be ready...Wendy is here. She is his twin sister."

A Grandmother

Irene Findlay

Some look upon grandmotherhood as a time to be dreaded. Having lived through childhood, girlhood, adulthood and motherhood, I embarked upon the next hood about eight years ago.

I cannot describe the proud feeling as I gazed on our first grandchild. It seemed such a short time since our own daughter had been as small as her daughter was now. The baby even resembled her mother. Watching each grandchild toddle through life's stages, I feel the same joy I experienced at the time of each birth.

Grandchildren have a way of lifting a grandmother to the height of an Albert Einstein. Only recently I explained the principle of the steaming kettle to our four-year old grandson. He looked up at me with admiration and said, "Grandma, how come you know everything?"

A grandson or granddaughter is a wiggly joy, off in all directions at once. They have few inhibitions. At the age of two our grandson was sitting with us at a morning church service. He had been told by his mother to close his eyes and bow his head as the minister was going to pray. The prayer was long, very long, much too long for a two-year old. Little Gordie had had enough. A childish voice called out, "OK, that's enough. Let's sing a song now."

A ripple of delight flowed through the congregation. Even the minister chuckled. But his poor mother prayed she was hearing things.

I wouldn't like new grandmothers to think grandmotherhood is hair-raising at all times. There are many rewarding experiences. You learn to appreciate the world of nature as never before—wild strawberries in little dells, or a frog keeping cool under a pile of rocks, and the honey bee in the watering can. Roses you dearly prize will never have smelled so sweet until you have had one pushed up to your nose with, "Smell it, Grandma."

I have seen the world more sharply through the eyes of our grand-children. What a privilege to share their little ways before their parents take them home again. No one should fear such a beautiful time of life.

Ode to a Crocus

Eva Cookson

I saw a flock of ducks today
And argued with a crow;
He'd only stopped to fill his beak;
He still had far to go.

A gopher ran across the road,
Then sat down in the snow,
He only stopped to scratch his fleas,
And wait for grass to grow.

At my feet there opened up
A precious growing thing,
Furred against the lingering frost,
A miracle of spring.

Clasped in the azure mother cup
There lay a golden ring;
Promising future purple jewels,
To grace another spring.

Seasons

Phyllis Alcorn

As each season passes I'm always impressed,
And find it hard choosing the one I like best.
The cold, snowy winters; the warm, balmy spring;
Or summer; or autumn; and all that they bring.
For each one is different in some special way;
Each with its own beauty of nature's display.

There's nothing so fine as a warm day in spring
When the crocuses bloom and I hear robins sing.
When the breeze on my cheek smells of newly-turned earth.
It's a time meant for planting; of hope; and of birth.
I relax in the sunshine, and hear the soft-falling rain,
And am lulled by the chorus of frogs once again.
Oh, spring! Time of beauty!
Now who would protest
That this glorious season must surely be best?

Then the days slowly lengthen, don a summery sheen.
The hills, trees, and fields are a lush, vibrant green.
Now the air smells of roses, or newly-mown hay,
And the heat-waves dance silently during mid-day.
Long, hot afternoons spent under shade trees
With no sound but the birds and the humming of bees.
And who can forget those still summer nights?
The soft call of an owl; or a fire-fly's flight?
Oh, summer, sweet summer!
When put to the test,
It surely is clear summertime is the best.

But I always love autumn, with its bright, golden days.
Its sapphire-blue skies above leaf-strewn pathways.

When the trees are a mixture of scarlet aand gold;
The days filled with sunshine; the nights crisp and cold.
When the grass in the morning is frosty and white,
And the call of the wild geese is heard in the night.
With the rustle of dry grass, the rattle of leaves,
And the sighing and moaning of wind in the eaves.
Oh, autumn! You charmer! So regally dressed.
Who could possibly say this time is not best?

Then along comes the winter, and the first fall of snow
Transforming the mountains and valleys below
To a silvery fairyland, dazzling and bright,
And cloaking the world 'neath a blanket of white.
The soft wintery sunshine spills over the snow
Setting diamonds to sparkling beneath its pale glow.
It's a time of deep silence, of snowflakes, and storm,
And icicles that drip from the roof when it's warm.
Oh, winter! You jewel! Filled with splendor and rest.
Surely you are the season that I love the best.

The seasons slip by, each with treasures untold;
Each one somehow special, as I watch them unfold.
So how can I choose just what season is best
When they're all full of beauty, and equally blessed?

The Wearing of the Green

Sharleen M. Chevraux

I am Irish. I own two Irish setters, have a fondness for the colour green, the taste of Irish coffee and the sound of an Irish brogue. Despite these things, I hadn't paid much attention to my roots in the 'auld sod'. Then a leprechaun moved into our basement.

He didn't come uninvited although the invitation was only laughingly made at the time. We had been finishing our basement in a rough-hewn, pioneer style when we ran out of ideas for one wall. Our hired man suggested the use of the one remaining wall of an old house located on our property. The wall contained a picturesque front door and the whole thing looked like it might fit our decor. It did fit our space and was duly installed against the cement on the west side of the basement. Just one problem. What looked like a perfectly good door to our son Corey couldn't be opened. When he asked why, I said flippantly, "Oh, that's because it's the Leprechaun's Door and only he can open it." Corey asked a million questions about leprechauns.

"Leprechauns belong to the Little People," I said. "They dress all in green with pointed caps and pointed shoes. They live in Ireland and guard pots of gold at the end of the rainbow."

"Then why do we have a leprechaun's door?"

"Well, I'm Irish and if a leprechaun ever gets tired of living in Ireland, he might like to come here," I answered, somewhat lamely.

It must have struck Herbert, the leprechaun, a bit differently. He moved in soon after our conversation. We didn't realize it for a time and that annoyed him. When leprechauns come into people's homes they demand immediate respect and attention. If they don't get it, they begin playing pranks.

At first, it was only the odd thing or two out of place, but when items actually began to disappear I still didn't tumble to the reason. I began to find green crayon marks on papers, walls, even furniture. I was sure it was Corey, but he stoutly denied it. For some reason a strange chant began running through my mind.

"Shamrocks, shillelaghs, leprechauns, shamrocks, shillelaghs,..." I was on the way downstairs. Out of the corner of my eye, I caught sight of the basement wall closing. "Leprechauns," I shouted, understanding at last.

Since then I've gotten to know Herbert quite well. He's an irascible little fellow with a wizened brown face and a traditionalist attitude. I can't imagine how he ever got the courage to emigrate. He insisted on my leaving him a bowl of milk every day, even though he detests milk, just because that is what a resident leprechaun should have. The day a mouse drowned in the bowl finally convinced him that the custom is silly. However, there's one thing we can't break him of. He resolutely insists that the whole household celebrate St. Patrick's Day with the "Wearing of the Green," and a loud cheer to the world. I don't dare offend him, so here goes:

Happy St. Patrick's Day!

Waiting for Spring

Sharleen M. Chevraux

A week ago I thought spring was here. Kids were wading in puddles along the street, usually the first sign. Then the deep freeze hit again and all those kids who had already dug out their skipping ropes and bags of marbles in anticipation of drying sidewalks had to put them away again.

Spring was my favorite season when I was a kid. My excitement began when the snow first started to soften. That was snowball time. We stock-piled dozens of them in snowforts and waited gleefully for the first human targets to show. We built snowmen too, scrounging in Mom's button bag for the eyes, nose and a mouth and invading Dad's cup-board for a pipe and his old battered hat. Almost before we could get Frosty finished, the first little trickles of water would appear and we'd follow their wriggles with delight.

A boy who lived across the street from me was a genius at making bridges and dams across tiny rivers that formed in our yard. He taught me how to place pebbles and twigs so the water formed into pools that grew until they spilled over and we had to start again.

Spring hurried then. Water poured into ditches and potholes to form puddles for wading all the way from home to the school yard and back. Our favorite game was to see how high the water could come before it spilled over and soaked our feet.

It was no time at all until the sidewalks were dry and we borrowed piec-es of chalk to draw hop-scotch and marble rings. We chanted skipping songs and dug out our bikes.

Our first bicycle rides each spring took us to Lover's Lane where the pussy willows grew or along the railroad tracks to pick crocuses. We rode there through drying puddles, with cool spring breezes vying with the warming sun—one saying take your jackets off and the other saying no, not yet. We usually did it anyway until our mothers caught us and ordered us into our coats again.

As spring merged into early summer, we began to haunt the old fair grounds watching for young pigweeds big enough for picking. We filled big bags with them and took them home to eat as spring's best delicacy—lamb's quarters.

I'm still waiting to feel the excitement of spring. It'll come again this year. I know it will.

Blue Promise

Eva Cookson

A living bit of summer blue
Rested on my fence today;
Fluffed his wings, and sang a song,
Before he flew away.

Did he sing an ode to Spring?
Or comment on the weather?
It mattered not. He left for me
A tiny bright blue feather.

The robins still are on their way.
The larks have not arrived.
But his message in my hand I hold
It's Spring, and I've survived !

Unforgettable Summers

Doris M. Saunders

School was out for the summer holidays!

There was time to run barefoot in the warm grass or wade in puddles after a shower. We could run down to the "Crick" to find the first violet, shooting star, or rose. There, too, we found the tangy wild strawberries and the sweet saskatoons. We could dabble in the creek and wile away time trying to catch silver minnows or cool our feet in the squishy mud.

We did have some work to do. Someone had to ride the horse to guide him as he pulled the cultivator down the rows of trees or garden. There was hoeing to do, too. We had a half mile of driveway with trees planted along one side as well as those planted around our house yard. They had to be cultivated and hoed to keep the weeds from choking them out.

My brother and I hunted gophers during the summer. We each had gopher traps with chains fastened to a pointed wooden stake. We walked the fence lines and pasture looking for gopher holes. When we found one that seemed to be in use, we carefully set the trap. We stepped on the end of the trap to open the jaws. While it was open, we set the trigger carefully so the jaws didn't close on our fingers. The trap was placed at the entrance of the gopher's den and the stake was pounded into the ground with a rock.

Later in the day we might find that the gopher had set off the trap and buried it in the dirt. If we had caught a gopher and it was still alive, we had to kill it by hitting its head with a stake. We had to take its tail as we were paid five cents for every three tails we were able to show at accounting time. To get the tail off you held it between your two fore-fingers and whirled the gopher about your head until the tail came off. Saving tails was how we earned our spending money.

Sometimes we were able to go bathing if the older kids were going to the "Ole swimming hole" in the creek. It had a muddy bottom but it was wet and cool after a hot day. My cousin tried to help me learn to float and swim but I was scared and couldn't get the hang of it. It wasn't until I was twelve and went to a C.G.I.T. camp that I learned.

Another joy of summer was a chance to go to camp with other girls. To sleep out in a tent, play together, have Bible study outside, swim and eat enormous meals was great fun. We always learned some new handicrafts to show on our return.

The campfires were especially memorable. There by the crackling bonfire we presented our skits and sang our songs. And as the sun cast long rays across the surface of the lake and disappeared behind the hills, we had evening worship and sang "Taps". We were thrilled as the echoes answered us from across the lake. It was an unforgettable experience of summer holidays.

The Golden Time

Sharleen M. Chevraux

Frantic, frustrating, fulfilling! It's harvest time again.

I am that not-so-rare creature called a town girl who married a farmer without knowing anything about farm life—its joys or its hardships. And many facets of the life still remain outside my ken. I have not yet mastered the mysteries of harrowing versus cultivating, rodweeding or discing. But I have learned perhaps the most important fact of all—the deep, soul-satisfying significance of harvest.

There is a growing excitement as the hot summer days of August complete the maturation of the crops—wheat, barley and canola on our farm. The men become tense, excited, a bit edgy. The combines and swathers are pulled out of the shed to be serviced, repaired, checked. Nothing must break down during the few short weeks that harvest is possible.

Evenings are spent tramping the fields, watching for signs that the grain is ready for the swather. Suddenly the time seems long—too long to wait, and short—too short to get everything ready. Then the evening finally comes. "That barley field will be ready by Tuesday." Only two more days to go. Last minute repairs—a furious rush for parts that have been ordered but haven't arrived. A sudden discovery. "That belt looks like it won't last through harvest. Better get another just in case."

Weather reports become all important. I've learned that one major duty of farm wives at this time is to listen to, read and watch weather reports as often as they are available.

Monday night. Rain is forecast. An anxious evening—half hoping that rain will fall, (it could help fill the heads of those crops not yet ready) and half hoping it won't so the men can get started.

Tuesday morning. No rain but a heavy dew. Swathing is delayed until noon. The tempo of work picks up but won't reach its height until the combines are also working, several days later.

At last all the machinery rolls and harvest is really here. Now there is a never-ending list of things for wives to do. Make meals. Pack lunches. Fill water jugs. Take grain samples to town to be tested. Snatch a few minutes to ride the combine or the truck hauling the grain to bins. Back to the meals again.

Meals. That is one of the best of all times at harvest. Dinner in the field, served hot and eaten picnic style among the swathes in the shade of the combine.

Making meals is no problem, but packing them and keeping them hot is. Boxes and jars, wax paper and foil wrap are laid out. Spill-proof salt and pepper shakers, sealed dishes of butter, small, individual packages of bread, dishes and cutlery—all assembled and packed. Then comes the food. Lots of it. More than we could normally eat in two meals, but harvesting is hungry work and so is watching it. Perhaps it is a roast today with potatoes and gravy, two kinds of vegetables, and pie for dessert. Or maybe fried chicken, or hamburger, or sausages. Maybe a baked pudding or cake and fruit. Into boxes it goes. Now we're ready. Oops! Forgot the tea or the coffee or the milk or the kool-aid. Everyone of us has a preference. The jars are filled, packed, and we're away.

Children clamber into the car or the truck, with careful instructions not to put their feet in the dinner, and we set out to find the men. Normally I know the field they're in but sometimes they fool me. They've moved and I have to search until I find them.

Even when we reach the field, it is such a maze of corners, bush patches and sloughs that it may take some time before I actually spot the combines—one on one side of the field and one on the other. Nothing to do but choose a spot half way between and begin laying out the food while the combines make their ponderous way in my direction— feeding on the broad swathes with a continuous, fascinating hunger as they come.

The trucks arrive and soon a group of dusty people are gathered— sprawling against the swathes, leaning on the combines or trucks—all with heaping plates and healthy appetites. It is peaceful, serene. The sun burns and shimmers while a breeze fans us gently—just enough to keep the wasps attracted by the smell of food from settling down. An indistinct hum of insects—a few bird songs—and silence. Conversation is sparse and lazy. For a few minutes there is no need for hurry or noise.

Those short periods of comradeship, of golden peace, can be compared to few other moments in life. There is a satisfaction, a love, a warm oneness with nature that is rare in our world of hustle-bustle. But they end too soon.

The hungry giants snort back to life and begin again their gorging. The trucks race to keep up—filling and unfilling their boxes with golden grain. I hasten to pick up the remains of dinner, repack the dishes and head for home. If I am quick enough I will have time to ride the combine or act as truck "swamper" for awhile before supper and lunches need to be made.

There is an excitement composed of dust, heat, hurry and monotony that goes with harvest. The haulers sit for long, slow minutes waiting for the grain hoppers to fill. Then they must speed to the combines, driving with precision and care while the grain spews forth, waiting for the honk which means "hopper empty" A rush to the bins and a quick trip back. A new load and long, slow minutes of waiting. The combines go round and round in an ever diminishing circuit only to move and begin again.

But harvest is more than these things. It is watching the swathes disappear; watching the bins fill. It is listening for combines in the late evening; watching isolated lights move slowly across a darkened field. It is running outside to feel the grass and know how much longer the men can work. It is satisfaction and fulfillment. The crops are in. One year's work is safely done.

Caught by Winter

Phyllis Alcorn

In this country, winter can arrive any time after Labor Day. Whenever it comes, I'm always caught with my cabbages out!

It doesn't matter how long the nice weather lasts, there are always jobs left undone when the first snow falls. It might be a few acres of combining, the vegetable garden to be cultivated, or that quarter mile of snow fence to put up.

How many times have I been caught with geraniums out and found the dirt to transplant them frozen solid beneath a layer of white stuff? How many hours have I spent tramping through the drifts hunting for lost garden gloves, or an extension cord? Often I have been forced to go the entire winter without knowing where I left my ladder, the booster cable, or a good set of wrenches.

The cold and snow always seem to arrive the day before I plan to dig that last row of carrots, or bring in the dry wood for the fireplace. If Indian summer lingered until Christmas the garage door still wouldn't be fixed, that new shed wouldn't be put up, the storm windows wouldn't be put on and the tractor would still have summer fuel.

The first storm of the season usually blows in the day we move the cattle home, or fix the well, or clean the sewer. If I start painting the fence one warm autumn morning, there'll be a blizzard by nightfall.

I can't remember a time when we had everything winterized BEFORE winter set in. There are always windows to be washed, the chicken house to be banked, or a half row of turnips still in the garden. To climb a snow-covered roof, straddle the frosty peak, and secure the T.V. antenna with numb fingers becomes a triumph of will-power.

It's the season for hot words and cold hands as we drag in that last sack of spuds, thaw those frozen water lines and change over to winter fuel and rough tires. As you search for that lost scoop-shovel or wrestle with frozen garden hose, remember you're not alone. We all get caught, without fail.

Reflections at the Cenotaph

Doris Wagar

The wind is cold to-day. Every passing year it seems to get colder. I am alone because the others felt it was too cold to come out. It bothers our joints you know. I come because I still remember the faces behind the names, and my memories are very precious to me. I never saw you grow old and tired as I am, so for this short time together we are young again.

You, Johnny, were some hot baseball pitcher. Remember how mad the players on the other teams were, when a kid like you fanned their best players? We were so proud of you. We cheered ourselves hoarse. At the dance all the girls crowded around you just to be near a hero. You loved it, and we loved you, Johnny.

Mickey, how you loved to dance. You were so strong and graceful. We made some pair, you and I, out on the floor, swaying to the music. I wonder in your secret heart, did you dream of becoming a dancer? You never said. We couldn't talk about such impossible things when we were young. A steady job was the greatest dream for most of us. I guess that was the reason it was so easy to persuade you to march off to battle.

Do you want to know something, fellows? All the things they promised wouldn't happen if you laid down your lives, have happened. Our children have no jobs. Our politicians seem to be out of touch with reality. There are so many wars going on, that I don't know who is fighting who, or why. Enough of this, I didn't come here to complain to you.

Billy, how you loved to laugh. I can still hear it booming through the halls of the high school. You always had a practical joke to play on some one. I guess life played the biggest practical joke of all on you. You never had time to get married and have children. Since you had no brothers or sisters, who is going to remember you when I am gone. You will be another name on a piece of stone—as though you had never lived at all.

They aren't having any ceremony here this year. The young people don't come any more. They are busy trying not to become like you. I hope their ways work better than ours. If I was younger, I would join them and shout and scream at the uselessness of it all.

The rich and greedy fight for power, and the young and beautiful die for ideals. We were so young and trusting, listening as the preacher shouted: "Render unto Caesar the things that are Caesar's." He never told us the world is full of Caesars; always has been and always will be. I am beginning to think one Caesar isn't one bit better than another.

Boy, that wind is cold! It makes my eyes water so I can't see the names on the stone. I'll go home now, but I'll be back next year. If I am still around and if there is a next year.

Catching Christmas

Betty Walsh

I never know just when or how it's going to arrive. One year it came in the middle of November. Another year it was on the afternoon of the day before Christmas.

As for how it comes—well it has never come in exactly the same way. In the same place—yes. Most often in my own home or in church, in a store or collecting the mail or baking cookies.

Once I was on my knees scrubbing the kitchen floor when a beautiful Christmas hymn issued forth on the radio and my daughter and I joined in the singing. Sitting back on my heels, it hit me, right then and there, that glorious, glowing, almost impossible to describe feeling.

The time I thought it wasn't coming, it arrived very simply. I was walking uptown on the afternoon of Christmas Eve. It was a still, crisp day with fat, fluffy snowflakes floating down. A couple of cars of folk I knew passed and waved. And what do you know—I'd got it.

Often I have found it in other people's eyes. In my son's eyes as he concluded his recitation at a Christmas concert. In my granddaughter's eyes as she explained all about Santa Claus. Or in my husband's eyes as we talk of Christmases past.

Many times it has arrived at Christmas Concert, especially in the Nativity scene. The children, so solemn, yet never far from nervous giggles. Joseph standing by, somehow imbued with the wonder of it all. Mary, somehow managing to convey the special feeling of a new mother. The shepherds, in awe and confusion. The wise men, trying not to trip over long robes as they present their gifts.

Then I've found it on T.V. in a show that touched me in just the right way. Or in writing a letter or addressing a card or wrapping a gift. The list of where gets longer each year but the feeling is always the same.

It's now the middle of December and so far it's not here. There have been a few little nearly-here tingles. But so far that real "Joy to the World" happy and grateful and blessed and loved and loving feeling isn't here yet.

But it'll come. It always has and it always will. Sometime soon, I know I'll catch Christmas.

O Christmas Tree

Doris M. Saunders

I was a small girl living on the prairie where few trees grew. We had no tree we could chop down or buy for Christmas, so we decided to make one. We drilled holes in a pole at intervals and inserted pieces of wood for branches. The branches looked stiff but when the trunk was wound with green tissue and each branch with green fringed strips, it would do. It stood ceiling high in a corner of the dining room.

We carefully cut and pasted red and green tissue paper chains together and draped the branches. A tinsel star on the top and looped strings of tinsel caught the lamplight, twinkling like the gleam in our eyes as we beheld our masterpiece. No Christmas tree could have been more enchanting. There were gaily wrapped gifts under it for us to shake, squeeze and imagine what was inside. What a splendid tree!

Many years later another Christmas tree reflected the love of another child. I was teaching by this time and as Christmas time grew nearer, anxiety grew in the blue eyes of one small grade one boy.

He was an only child who lived with his parents on a bush farm down near the river. They were poor—so poor, it was whispered, that his mother made her voluminous bloomers from Robin Hood flour sacks. Mrs. Cameron was a very big woman who on cold snowy days drove her son to school in a homesteader's bob sleigh. They had no money for a gift for the teacher. As the other pupils whispered to one another about what they were getting me, Colin's anxiety grew.

In talking about Christmas traditions and customs, I had mentioned the fact that at my home we could not go out and chop down a spruce tree for Christmas. A little gleam seemed to cross my little pupil's face. The next day his mother secretly whispered to me.

"If I bring you a spruce tree would you be able to take it home?"

I had to travel about 600 miles by train but I smiled and answered, "If I can put it in my suitcase, I certainly will."

I noticed my little pupil's spirits had risen by the next day and he was able to join in with the Christmas excitement.

The day of the Christmas concert arrived at last. Colin came to school smiling, his eyes brimming with excitement. "Teacher, this is for you," he said proudly as he presented his gift—a perfect little spruce tree.

"Oh, how lovely!" I exclaimed. "Thank you very much, Colin. Won't it look beautiful when it's trimmed! My folks will be surprised when I take this home."

Later, it was carefully packed for the long journey. I bought some tiny decorations and at Christmas my little tree on the table glowed with love.

I have since seen many beautifully decorated trees, both natural and artificial, but none have meant more to me than these two.

That Christmas Feeling

Sharleen M. Chevraux

A soft glow of colored lights shining through lightly falling snow. O Little Town of Bethlehem, The First Noel, We Three Kings of Orient Are...sounding clear but distant in the crisp night air. Warmth and love and excitement and secrets and delicious, tantalizing smells. It's Christmas.

I can't remember a time when I didn't love Christmas. As a child my anticipation of its coming began with the first flakes of winter snow and built almost to bursting through the weeks that followed. There were so many things to do . Help Mom with the baking. Make chains of colored paper to hang above the door. Find the old Christmas cards and cut them into new patterns to decorate walls. Practice for the Christmas concerts at the church and the school. Make gifts for my family. Trim the tree.

Is there anything more magic than a Christmas tree? Ours always had a tinsel star on top; tiny glass acorns tucked among the branches; blue, green, and red balls hanging from the tips of boughs; and lights twinkling everywhere, reflected in shimmering silver icicles. Occasionally we'd even have some candy canes hanging tantalizingly out of reach. It was fairyland come true.

And the days quickened.

The Christmas concert came. I remember the shabby red curtain that sagged and squeaked as it was pulled open to a sea of waiting faces. And my happy pride as I raced through my recitation and searched for my mother's smile. I remember the tickle in my nose that made me sneeze over the Baby Jesus in his cradle just as the Three Wise Men approached. One of them giggled and forgot his lines while the teacher glared. I remember the carols that we sang with such off-key gusto and joy. And then Jingle Bells, Jingle Bells, louder and louder until Santa came bursting through the door with a "Ho-Ho-Ho," bringing bags of candy, oranges and nuts with a tiny present for each of us.

By Christmas Eve our family had come—my aunt and uncle and cousins. They brought new laughter and excitement and a box of presents to add to the pile already gathering under our tree. We whispered and giggled our secrets and our dreams and tried to stay up as late as we could, but finally our parents could stand it no longer.

"Off to bed with you," they'd say. "If you don't get to sleep soon, Santa won't come."

Into our pyjamas and out we'd come again, this time to lay our stockings on the back of the chesterfield and put out a cookie and milk treat for Santa Claus.

"There's no use hoping that old sizzerbill, Santa, will come," my father would tease. "I'm going to stay awake all night just to chase him away. He didn't bring me anything but a rotten potato last year."

"No! No!" we'd cry with delight, knowing by his crinkling laugh lines that he'd never do such a thing. And off we'd go to bed, not to sleep for awhile, but to lie in quivering anticipation instead.

***

"It's five o'clock," my cousin would whisper. "Are you awake? Let's go see what Santa brought."

"You kids go back to sleep," my mother would call. "You can't get up before 6:00."

What an unending hour that was! Eyes fixed on the luminous dial of the clock, we wriggled and squirmed and whispered and at last the seconds and minutes ticked by.

We dashed to the living room, grabbed our stockings and raced to our parents' room.

"See, Mom! See, Dad! Look what we've got." Crayons, coloring books, pencils, candies, nuts, and a book or two would be tumbled on top of their bed, while they looked and laughed and Father would say, "Did that old sizzerbill leave anything in my sock?"

"There's a lump in it," we'd say.

"Probably a piece of coal or another potato," he'd pretend to grump, as he'd turn it upside down. And sure enough, that's just what it would be.

When the adults had their dressing gowns on and a cup of coffee in their hands, it was present opening time. Our gifts were usually little things but—oh!—we did have fun. We'd take a peek, exclaim with delight and run to kiss the giver. In an hour or two, there was nothing left under the tree but a welter of paper and ribbons and bows.

At nine o'clock, the Queen would speak and we listened every year. Then breakfast time and after that, back to our toys and games. The adults always joined us for part of the day, at least, and when they tired of our toys, we played cards or games with them. We teased and talked and squabbled over toys and laughed while the hours sped by and the smell of turkey roasting in the oven tickled our nostrils with joy.

Turkey! Brown, crisp, tender and oozing with taste. Mashed potatoes, gravy, dressing, salads, vegetables. My tummy aches with remembered bliss. And Christmas Pudding! Tart, rich and smothered in sauce. We ate and ate and ate.

I'm not a girl anymore. I have children of my own. When December comes and they begin to poke and pry and whisper and giggle to themselves as they help me bake and shop and decorate, I join in the fun. We practice for the Christmas concert and wait for Santa Claus. We listen to Silent Night through the sofly falling snow. We spread our stockings and give our gifts and leap out of bed at 6 o'clock.

It's Christmas.

The Special Christmas Tree

Violet M. Copeland

We had returned to the homestead that year, after living in small towns; everything was new and strange—and inconvenient. Water did not come from a tap or a cistern pump, but was hauled in barrels, and carefully hoarded. We could not walk to school but had a bumpy drive in a democrat. Milk and butter came, not in handy cartons, but after a struggle with cows or churns. Fuel had to be chopped, sawed, split and carried in, and ashes had to be carried out. Registers for heat were just a memory.

Christmas was coming, with its familiar excitement as we began making gifts and whispering secrets.

Then the problem arose...

"Where will we get the Christmas tree?"

An innocent question from a small sister, but it set us all thinking. Where, indeed, in this strange land of poplar and willow, with the only available evergreen in the cemetery, miles away?

"Where do they get the school tree?" Mother asked.

"Some are shipped in but they are expensive," Papa said.

Our hearts sank at that word "expensive." These were the thirties, when every penny counted. Papa explained that we couldn't have an evergreen this year. Maybe next year.

We were stunned. No tree for the sparkly angel, and the glass birds, and the golden bell that really rang? No reason to make our crayon-paper garlands, or the popcorn chains?

It just wouldn't be Christmas.

Mother looked thoughtful.

It was three days before Christmas, and we were still feeling lost, when she brought in the tiny poplar.

We just looked at her. A poplar wasn't a Christmas tree!

"Get busy!" she instructed and in no time had us cutting long, fringed strips of paper from last year's green tissue paper, making paste, winding the branches, while everybody carolled. Surprisingly, the tree turned green and the fringes made incredible pine needles. We really had a tree after all, a beautiful tree.

Christmas, 1930's Style

Doris Likness

Two small boys pressing button noses against frosty windows began to call out excitedly: "Mom, MOM, Kris's coming!"

I joined them at the peephole. A box-sled and team were toiling through the deep drifts toward our small home. Time to get the coffee on to warm up the frozen driver.

Bitter, blizzardly weather had been with us for some time. It was December 27, and we hadn't really celebrated Christmas. The long trip to our store post-office had been out of the question to take, but today Kris, our bachelor neighbor, had given it a try. After his cup of steaming coffee and a fresh bun, he left for his bachelor abode and with a little one on a chair on either side, I eagerly inspected the goodies he had brought.

With delight we pounced upon the Eaton order, and noticed with joy three other Christmas parcels. As we tore off the wrappings, I hid a few gifts for the small stockings that would be hung that night. My husband came in from doing chores and joined in. No longer did we mourn our snowy isolation. We were loved and remembered, and the Christmas spirit warmed our hearts anew.

I was a city girl from the west coast who had come to Alberta, April 1926, because teachers were needed here. I taught straight through until Christmas to make up for teacherless months prior to my coming. The following October I married a young farmer. Difficult times came upon us as crops failed year after year, and our grand dreams lay in the dust.

Our two-roomed home lacked modern conveniences; our Ford stood idle in the shed, later becoming a "Bennett Buggy," the chassis drawn by horses. A five gallon can of cream brought the sum of one dollar, and butter which I made and packaged, ten cents a pound. Eggs sold for five cents a dozen.

We managed to stay off the dole with my teacher's salary of $80.00 per month. It was a five-mile trip by horseback or buggy to my school, pleasant enough in fine weather, but an ordeal in winter. I resorted then to a small covered-in sled.

Now we were celebrating Christmas several days late. It had made no difference to my house-bound little ones. We had shared the Christmas story and listened with radio headphones to beautiful Christmas music. We were prepared. On December 28, squeals of delight would herald surprises in each bulging stocking. All was well in our household and 1932 was another year of hope.

The Christmas Turkey

Myrna Mackey

Christmas always took so long to arrive and it went by so fast. Mom took a long time to get ready. She made Christmas cakes and fruit pudding in advance and stored the pudding in jars under our bed. The cakes were there too, wrapped in wax paper and put in Nabob tins with roses on them. I always wanted to taste it but she said, "It's not cured yet." If she even heard paper rattling by our bed, she would say, "You're not into the cake, are you?" I guess it had to cure in the dark.

We always had turkey too, but I failed to see how the one we had in our yard could look like the one Grandma took out of her oven on Christmas day. She would open the oven door and pull out the roaster. There he would be (turkeys were always a He) all brown and shiny, smelling so good with dressing oozing out around the string that tied his legs.

Grandma would poke him with a fork. "Ya, he's done," she'd say, and smile. Replacing the cover, she would set the heavy roaster on the reservoir.

Our turkey was big and black, with lots of feathers and big ugly feet, and a nose that hung down over his mouth. I had to watch out for him because he bit. I took a stick when I went to the toilet because he would come out of the trees and chase me back to the house. Most of the time, I made it safely behind the screen door just before he got to me. Then I could yell at him and wave the stick. He would strut, and gobble and stamp his feet.

"Don't tease the turkey!" Mom would yell.

Boy! He teased me first.

One day my brother was playing outside and the turkey sneaked up on him and knocked him down, scratched his back, pecked him around his neck and tore his coat. My brother screamed until Mom came out of the house and took the broom to the turkey.

When my dad came in, she said, "That's it! We'll have that turkey for Christmas."

I wasn't happy with the idea since I couldn't see how our turkey could possibly look like the one Grandma had for Christmas. The next day the turkey didn't chase me. When I asked about him, I was told he had been put in a box to be taken to Grandma's house. I went, too, with my dad and a big cardboard box in the back of the horse-drawn sleigh. That turkey was so quiet. He never gobbled or anything all the way to town. When we got there, Grandpa came out and put the box in the shed.

"He'll stay frozen in there," he said.

The turkey still didn't make any noise. I always cried when I got frozen.

Every day I asked, "How many more days?" and Mom would say seven or four or three. Finally it was Christmas. We got to Grandma's house and everybody was there—aunts, uncles, cousins—people everywhere and everybody talking at once. Grandpa sat in his rocking chair by the Christmas tree with a small barrel close by.

"Herring," he said. "From my brother in Norway."

From the smell of it, I wouldn't have traded it for any of the good stuff spread out on the table like lefsa, rosettes, krum kaka, Christmas cake and jars of pudding.

I was told to get out of the kitchen but I wanted to see Grandma open the oven. When she put down the door and took the lid off the roaster, there he was, all brown and smelling so good, with string tied around his legs. Just like last Christmas.

What Every Little Girl Wants for Christmas

Rose Marie Thompson

Dolls used to be beautiful of face and ordinary of body. They were neither buxom of figure nor anatomically correct. Neither were they "expecting." You could tell the difference between a boy doll and a girl doll by the clothes they wore and the length of hair. Girl dolls had long hair and wore dresses. Boy dolls had short hair and wore pants. When you took their clothes off, they all looked the same, a basic baby body with no distinguishing features. That is, except for one doll. One of my first. That one was obviously a girl. It was called a "Wettums Doll." This little beauty came with only two items, a diaper and a baby bottle. I would ask some unsuspecting person to hold my dolly, put the bottle of water in her mouth and wait for them to jump up as the doll wet their lap.

I considered myself a doll expert in my childhood. By my fifth birthday, I was the proud owner of twenty-three dolls. I had so many because my Mother had none. In a poor family, dolls were not considered one of the necessities of life. My Mother lived vicariously through me by buying me every doll she saw.

My third Christmas, I received a much loved doll Mother made using a bleached sugar sack. A red and white gingham dress clothed her and black, curly wool covered her head. Embroidered, blue eyes stared, and blood red lips puckered, as she sat beneath the tree Christmas morning. My eyes lit up like the candles on the tree when I spied her and I christened her "Aunt Minnie." My real life Aunt Minnie forever wondered where I saw any resemblance.

On my fourth birthday, I was taken to the toy department in the Hudson's Bay Store in Calgary. Hundreds of dolls crowded the shelves from ceiling to floor.

Mother said, "You may pick any doll you like."

Her eyes settled on a three foot tall bride doll in flowing white gown. It was the centerpiece of the display.

I wandered the aisles until I came upon a very small, very black, baby doll.

"I want this one Mom. This nigger baby."

Used to nigger-toes at Christmas; nigger-babies as candy; and nigger-children in stories like "Little Black Sambo," and considering this was the prairies in 1940, I didn't know that I should probably have called it a coloured baby. I had never seen a coloured person, or a coloured child, much less a coloured doll, and that little honey stood out from all the rest. That this doll cost $1.98 and the one Mom had her eye on was worth $20.00 meant nothing. Once I had seen that "nigger baby," none other would do. I nearly broke my Mother's heart by rejecting the one she wanted!

The Christmas I was four, I reached the pinnacle of doll ownership. I received my Eaton's Beauty Doll.

The mail order Christmas catalogues arrived in early fall. We thumbed through the pages until they were well worn, each one dreaming of what we would like for Christmas. There were lots of dolls, but one stood out. Her face was a thing of beauty with delicate nose, red bow mouth and blue eyes that opened and closed. Golden curls, tied with pink ribbon, crowned her head. She wore pink organza and lace with white shoes and socks to complete her outfit.

"Dear Santa, I have been a good girl. For Christmas I would like an Eaton's Beauty Doll. I will leave you some milk and cookies. Love Rose Marie."

The weeks between when I mailed that letter and when Christmas arrived dragged on forever.

At last, it was Christmas morning.

At 4 a.m., my brother and I made it halfway down to the living room when the creaking of the stairs brought a sleepy, "It's too early to get up children. Santa hasn't been here yet," from Father.

We trudged back up the cold stairs to slip into still warm beds. Slumber overtook us. When we awoke, we could hear Mother sliding the turkey into the oven. The aroma of frying bacon curled up the stairs and tickled our nostrils.

On flying feet we raced down the stairway, pausing in the kitchen to kiss Mother a Merry Christmas. Wood crackled in the stove and a red glow showed through the wide-open damper. Coffee gurgled in the pot.

With shining eyes we peered into the living room, lit only by the glow of scores of candles. Flakes of Lux soap, sprinkled atop a soap paste which had been smeared on the boughs to resemble snow, caught the flickers of candle light and a million tiny stars seemed to dance on the tree.

Hanging from the ceiling by a string was a dirigible, a replica of the "Hindenburg" which had crashed in 1937. It was just what my brother had asked for in his letter to Santa.

Beneath the tree, amidst the gaily wrapped parcels, sat "Beauty," for in my heart I had already named her.

It mattered little that there were other gifts for me that Christmas morning. Having gained my heart's desire, I wished for nothing more.

"Beauty" joined my doll family and except for an accident some months later in which her head was broken and fixed, she remained my favorite doll until my doll playing days were over.

To this day she remains in my heart, and I'm grateful for a more innocent time when a little girl's doll was also her best friend.

The Footprint

Betty Walsh

My sister Jack saw it first. There it was, distinct and easy to see in the grey-white ashes in the fireplace—a large footprint. We three girls gathered around and examined it carefully. It showed up clearly in the cold, clear light of that December morning. We squatted on the floor and studied this mysterious imprint.

It was a Christmas morning in England over half a century ago. With my two younger sisters, I had come into our parents' bedroom to join them and our brand new baby sister in the annual ritual of finding out just what Father Christmas had left in our stockings. At eight years old, I was big sister, followed by six-year-old Binkie and four-year-old Jackie. We usually scrambled right on the bed, lugging our bulging treasures, and, after wriggling into the bottom of the bed, began to unload our haul. But this new development had taken our minds off our stockings.

Jackie was the first to voice her opinion. "Ronnie said there isn't a Father Christmas. It's just your dad and mum. So how could it be his footprint?"

I was pretty certain it was Dad and Mum but I had been keeping my opinion to myself. Always willing to admit the possibility of something I didn't understand, I chimed in, "You know Ronnie is nearly always wrong. If it's not HIS footprint, whose is it?"

Ever the cynic, Binkie looked at our parents, "Did you step in the ashes, Dad?"

"Now what would I do that for," replied Dad. "Would I want ashes all over my boots?"

"Then it was you, wasn't it, Mum?"

"Certainly not. Do you think I have nothing better to do than play around in the ashes? Besides, the fire was still burning when I went to bed."

Jackie got up and stomped down the stairs, followed by Binkie. In a few moments they returned carrying an assortment of boots and shoes. One by one they solemnly fitted them into that big footprint.

But not one was anywhere near the right size. Leaving the boots and shoes in a heap on the hearth, they trailed downstairs again. They were gone longer this time, obviously looking for any footwear they'd overlooked. Charging upstairs, they triumphantly brought in Dad's big rubber boots. Surely they'd fit. But they didn't.

Sitting back on our heels, we looked at each other.

"Maybe there really is a Father Christmas," voiced Jackie.

"I didn't think there was, but I suppose there could be," mused Binkie.

As big sister, I settled it. "Of course there is. I told you so."

And with that out of the way, we climbed on the bed and began to unload our stockings.

Joy to the World

Doris A. Wagar

Christmas Eve 1942 was clear and cold, with an unrelenting north wind rattling the windows of the old Lamont hospital. The radiators hissed in a feeble attempt to keep out the creeping cold. Halls were dark and quiet, with only the bare bulb above a chart table casting it's inadequate light. The north windows were layered with frost,

There were only four sleeping patients on the ward that night—two cantankerous, homeless old ladies and a mother and her new born son.

As a defence against drafts, I wrapped an old blanket from the linen room around me. For the hundredth time I asked myself, "What am I doing in this God-forsaken place?" I really knew, though. Too young to enlist in the services, and no money to pay university fees, I really didn't have many choices. It was a start. I probably could have got married and raised chickens and children, but with the boys away at war, the choices weren't great there either.

Just then the baby in the nursery began to whimper. Even with the auxiliary heater the nursery was cold and drafty. After changing his diaper, I decided the best place for him was with me. I opened my sweater and placed his cold little body close to mine, then wrapped the blanket around us. It was against the rules, but who was there to see?

As I sat looking at the perfection of the child in my arms, my mind wandered. How strange I should be sitting here alone on Christmas Eve nurturing a small male child. Christmas at our house never said too much about the baby Jesus. It was a time of feverish preparation, followed by recovery from various over-indulgences. With no small children around, life seemed to lose some of its wonder after the demise of Santa Claus and the tooth fairy.

I could hear some noise at the other end of the hall, but since I had no patients down there, I paid no attention to it. If I was needed they would let me know. I didn't want to awaken the baby. I had decided to let his mother sleep in. It might be the last chance she had. With six children in ten years, she looked old and tired.

At six o'clock the cold silence was broken by the thirty voice Moravian Church choir from Bruderheim proclaiming Christ's joyous birth. As the sound arose again and again, I felt a warm aliveness bursting from within me. Overcome with emotion, I began to sob. The baby awakened, and gazed up at me with a look of wisdom. It seemed he knew what I was just learning.

When I took him to his mother, she also was crying. We looked wordlessly into each other's eyes, as if we shared some wondrous knowledge. I finished the morning in a trance. Sleep was impossible that day. I was afraid if I went to sleep, I would lose that feeling of joy, and be cold and empty again.

My life changed for me that Christmas morning. It was the beginning of humility. I understood what the angels meant so long ago, when they sang,
> "Joy to the world, the Lord is born
> Let earth receive her King."

DATE DUE